First Edition

P9-CEW-404

Common Core
Support Coach

TARGET

Foundational Mathematics 7

Dr. Jerry Kaplan
Senior Mathematics Consultant

Common Core Support Coach, Target: Foundational Mathematics, First Edition, Grade 7
T202NA   ISBN-13: 978-1-61997-978-9
Contributing Writers: TSI Graphics   **Cover Design:** Q2A/Bill Smith

Triumph Learning® 136 Madison Avenue, 7th Floor, New York, NY 10016

Contents

Computing Unit Rates

PLUG IN Using Ratios

A **ratio** compares two quantities. It can be expressed in different ways.

The ratio of apples to oranges is 8 to 3.

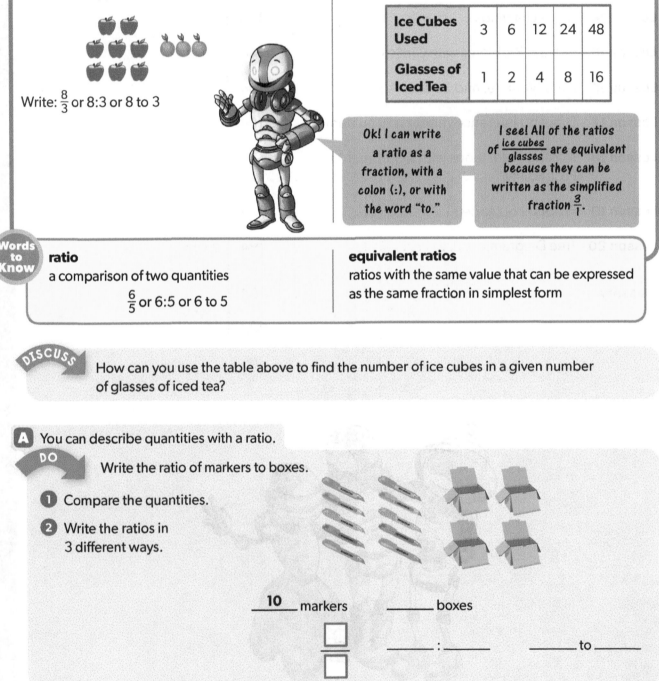

Write: $\frac{8}{3}$ or 8:3 or 8 to 3

Equivalent ratios can be written as the same fraction in simplest form. A table of equivalent ratios shows how two quantities are related.

Ice Cubes Used	3	6	12	24	48
Glasses of Iced Tea	1	2	4	8	16

Ok! I can write a ratio as a fraction, with a colon (:), or with the word "to."

I see! All of the ratios of $\frac{ice\ cubes}{glasses}$ are equivalent because they can be written as the simplified fraction $\frac{3}{1}$.

Words to Know

ratio
a comparison of two quantities
$\frac{6}{5}$ or 6:5 or 6 to 5

equivalent ratios
ratios with the same value that can be expressed as the same fraction in simplest form

DISCUSS

How can you use the table above to find the number of ice cubes in a given number of glasses of iced tea?

A You can describe quantities with a ratio.

DO Write the ratio of markers to boxes.

❶ Compare the quantities.

❷ Write the ratios in 3 different ways.

_____10_____ markers   _____ boxes

☐
☐   _____ : _____   _____ to _____

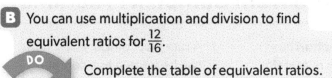

B You can use multiplication and division to find equivalent ratios for $\frac{12}{16}$.

DO Complete the table of equivalent ratios.

1 Multiply both quantities to find equivalent ratios.

2 Divide both quantities to find more equivalent ratios.

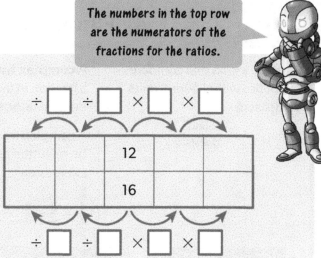

The numbers in the top row are the numerators of the fractions for the ratios.

$\div\square \ \div\square \ \times\square \ \times\square$

			12		
			16		

$\div\square \ \div\square \ \times\square \ \times\square$

C You can use equivalent ratios to solve problems.

DO Janet runs 2,640 feet in 5 minutes. Dan runs 1,730 feet in 3 minutes. If they keep the same paces, who would run farther in 15 minutes?

Janet's Running Times				
Feet	2,640			
Minutes	5	10	15	20

1 Write the ratio of feet to minutes for each person.

2 Complete the table to write equivalent ratios.

Dan's Running Times				
Feet	1,730			
Minutes	3	6	9	15

3 Use the table to compare the ratios.

_____ would run farther in 15 minutes. _____ would run 8,650 feet and _____ would run 7,920 feet.

DISCUSS How could you find the number of feet run for a number of minutes that is not in the table?

PRACTICE

Complete the table of equivalent ratios.

1

Feet	3	6	9	
Yards	1	2		

2

Text Messages	1	2		4
Cost ($)	0.20	**0.40**	0.60	

Solve.

3 Alex reads 12 pages in 10 minutes. Jenna reads 15 pages in 12 minutes. They are both reading a 60-page magazine. Who will finish reading the magazine first? _____

POWER UP Finding Rates from Complex Fractions

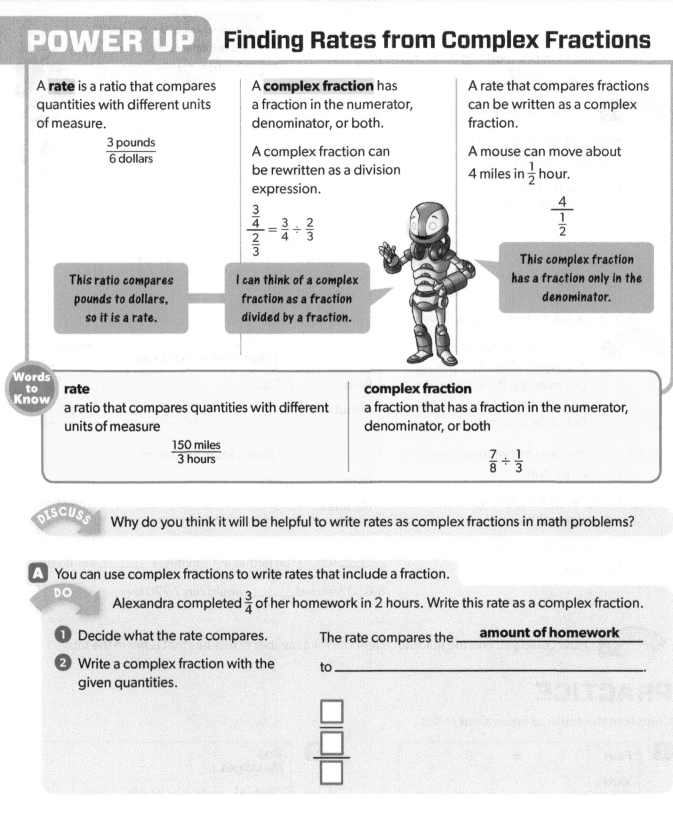

A **rate** is a ratio that compares quantities with different units of measure.

$$\frac{3 \text{ pounds}}{6 \text{ dollars}}$$

A **complex fraction** has a fraction in the numerator, denominator, or both.

A complex fraction can be rewritten as a division expression.

$$\frac{\frac{3}{4}}{\frac{2}{3}} = \frac{3}{4} \div \frac{2}{3}$$

A rate that compares fractions can be written as a complex fraction.

A mouse can move about 4 miles in $\frac{1}{2}$ hour.

$$\frac{4}{\frac{1}{2}}$$

This ratio compares pounds to dollars, so it is a rate.

I can think of a complex fraction as a fraction divided by a fraction.

This complex fraction has a fraction only in the denominator.

Words to Know

rate
a ratio that compares quantities with different units of measure

$$\frac{150 \text{ miles}}{3 \text{ hours}}$$

complex fraction
a fraction that has a fraction in the numerator, denominator, or both

$$\frac{7}{8} \div \frac{1}{3}$$

DISCUSS Why do you think it will be helpful to write rates as complex fractions in math problems?

A You can use complex fractions to write rates that include a fraction.

DO Alexandra completed $\frac{3}{4}$ of her homework in 2 hours. Write this rate as a complex fraction.

❶ Decide what the rate compares.

❷ Write a complex fraction with the given quantities.

The rate compares the ___**amount of homework**___

to _____.

$$\frac{\square}{\square}$$

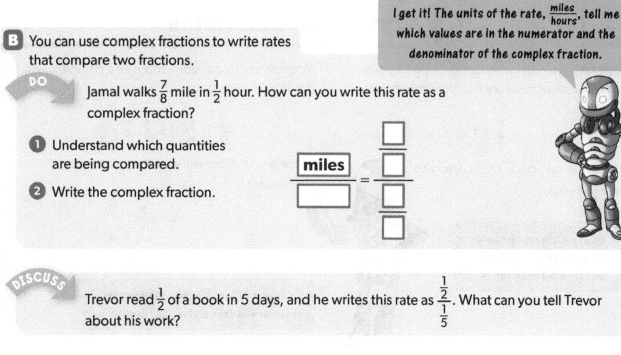

B You can use complex fractions to write rates that compare two fractions.

I get it! The units of the rate, $\frac{miles}{hours}$, tell me which values are in the numerator and the denominator of the complex fraction.

DO Jamal walks $\frac{7}{8}$ mile in $\frac{1}{2}$ hour. How can you write this rate as a complex fraction?

1 Understand which quantities are being compared.

2 Write the complex fraction.

$$\frac{\boxed{\text{miles}}}{\boxed{}} = \frac{\boxed{}}{\boxed{}}$$

DISCUSS Trevor read $\frac{1}{2}$ of a book in 5 days, and he writes this rate as $\frac{\frac{1}{2}}{\frac{1}{5}}$. What can you tell Trevor about his work?

PRACTICE

Write the rate as a complex fraction.

1 A recipe calls for $\frac{2}{3}$ cup of flour to make $\frac{1}{4}$ of a batch of cookies.

$$\frac{\boxed{2}}{\boxed{3}} \atop \overline{\boxed{} }$$

2 A band marched $\frac{3}{4}$ of the parade route in $\frac{2}{3}$ hour.

$$\frac{\boxed{}}{\boxed{}} \atop \frac{\boxed{}}{\boxed{}}$$

3 A car used $\frac{3}{5}$ of a tank of gas to travel $\frac{5}{8}$ of the total distance.

4 A sprinkler system uses $\frac{1}{3}$ gallon of water every $\frac{1}{5}$ hour.

READY TO GO   Computing Unit Rates

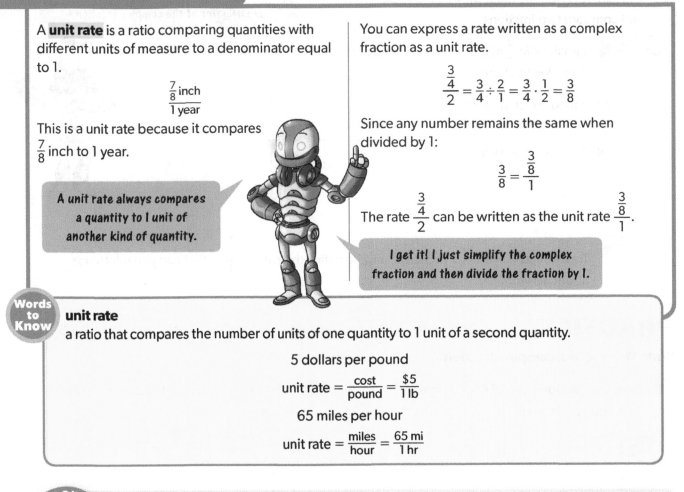

A **unit rate** is a ratio comparing quantities with different units of measure to a denominator equal to 1.

$$\frac{\frac{7}{8} \text{ inch}}{1 \text{ year}}$$

This is a unit rate because it compares $\frac{7}{8}$ inch to 1 year.

> A unit rate always compares a quantity to 1 unit of another kind of quantity.

You can express a rate written as a complex fraction as a unit rate.

$$\frac{\frac{3}{4}}{2} = \frac{3}{4} \div \frac{2}{1} = \frac{3}{4} \cdot \frac{1}{2} = \frac{3}{8}$$

Since any number remains the same when divided by 1:

$$\frac{3}{8} = \frac{\frac{3}{8}}{1}$$

The rate $\frac{\frac{3}{4}}{2}$ can be written as the unit rate $\frac{\frac{3}{8}}{1}$.

> I get it! I just simplify the complex fraction and then divide the fraction by 1.

Words to Know

unit rate
a ratio that compares the number of units of one quantity to 1 unit of a second quantity.

5 dollars per pound

$$\text{unit rate} = \frac{\text{cost}}{\text{pound}} = \frac{\$5}{1 \text{ lb}}$$

65 miles per hour

$$\text{unit rate} = \frac{\text{miles}}{\text{hour}} = \frac{65 \text{ mi}}{1 \text{ hr}}$$

DISCUSS   Why might it be helpful to find unit rates?

LESSON LINK

PLUG IN

A ratio compares two quantities. A ratio can be written in three ways.

$\frac{3}{5}$ 3:5   3 to 5

POWER UP

A ratio that includes a fraction can be written as a complex fraction.

$$\frac{\frac{2}{3}}{\frac{1}{6}}$$

GO!

> I see! I can use what I know about ratios and complex fractions to find unit rates. Then I can use unit rates to solve problems.

WORK TOGETHER

You can use labeled Fraction Strips to help you solve unit rate problems involving complex fractions.

Division lets me simplify fractions, even complex fractions! I can use fraction strips to model division.

- The rate of cups to hours is written as a complex fraction.
- The complex fraction is written as a division problem and simplified.
- The unit rate is $\frac{3}{1}$.
- The Fraction Strips model the problem.
- Tara will drink 3 cups of water in 1 hour.

Tara drinks 2 cups of water in $\frac{2}{3}$ hour. At this rate, how much water will Tara drink in an hour?

$$\frac{cups}{hours} = \frac{2}{\frac{2}{3}}$$

$$\frac{2}{\frac{2}{3}} = \frac{2}{1} \div \frac{2}{3} = \frac{2}{1} \times \frac{3}{2} = \frac{6}{2} = \frac{3}{1}$$

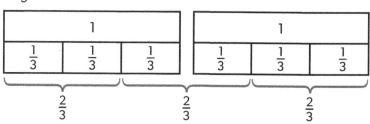

A You can use unit rates to solve problems.

DO

A recipe calls for $\frac{2}{3}$ cup of sugar to make $\frac{4}{5}$ gallon of iced tea. How much sugar is needed to make 1 gallon of iced tea?

Fraction Strips can be found on p. 209.

❶ Write the rate of sugar to iced tea as a complex fraction.

❷ Write the complex fraction as a division problem, then rewrite as multiplication.

❸ Divide both the numerator and the denominator by the denominator to find the unit rate.

$$\frac{sugar}{iced\ tea} = \frac{\frac{2}{3}}{\frac{4}{5}}$$

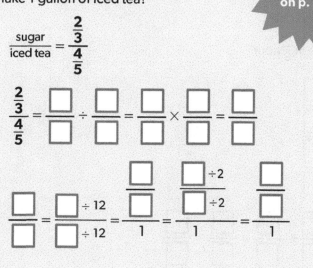

The unit rate is _____.

_____ cup of sugar is needed to make 1 gallon of iced tea.

DISCUSS

How can you be sure that you have found the unit rate?

PRACTICE

Fraction Strips can be found on p. 211.

Find the unit rate. Use Fraction Strips to help you.

1 A recipe calls for 5 eggs for every $\frac{1}{2}$ teaspoon of salt.

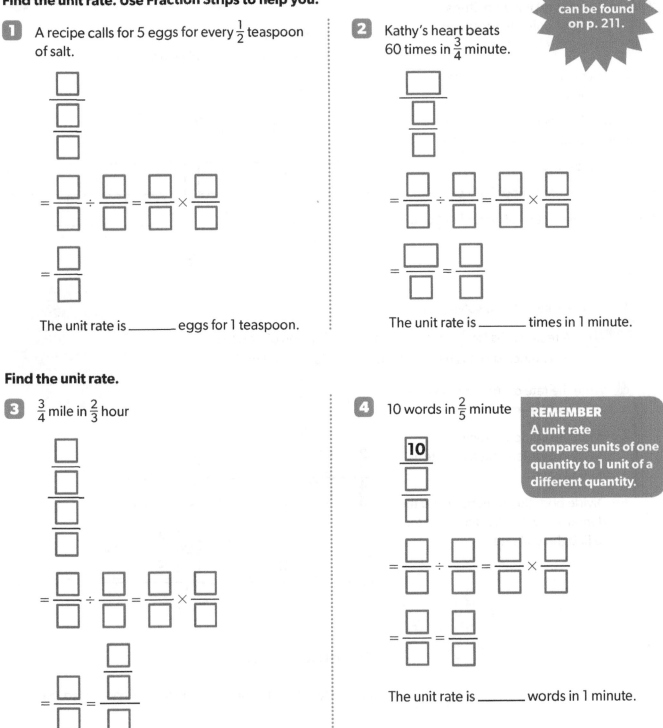

$$= \frac{\square}{\square} \div \frac{\square}{\square} = \frac{\square}{\square} \times \frac{\square}{\square}$$

$$= \frac{\square}{\square}$$

The unit rate is _____ eggs for 1 teaspoon.

2 Kathy's heart beats 60 times in $\frac{3}{4}$ minute.

$$= \frac{\square}{\square} \div \frac{\square}{\square} = \frac{\square}{\square} \times \frac{\square}{\square}$$

$$= \frac{\square}{\square} = \frac{\square}{\square}$$

The unit rate is _____ times in 1 minute.

Find the unit rate.

3 $\frac{3}{4}$ mile in $\frac{2}{3}$ hour

$$= \frac{\square}{\square} \div \frac{\square}{\square} = \frac{\square}{\square} \times \frac{\square}{\square}$$

$$= \frac{\square}{\square} = \frac{\square}{\square}$$

The unit rate is _____ miles in 1 hour.

4 10 words in $\frac{2}{5}$ minute

REMEMBER
A unit rate compares units of one quantity to 1 unit of a different quantity.

$$\frac{10}{\square}$$

$$= \frac{\square}{\square} \div \frac{\square}{\square} = \frac{\square}{\square} \times \frac{\square}{\square}$$

$$= \frac{\square}{\square} = \frac{\square}{\square}$$

The unit rate is _____ words in 1 minute.

Compare the unit rates.

5 Alice skates $\frac{2}{5}$ mile in $\frac{1}{5}$ hour. Elizabeth skates $\frac{2}{3}$ mile in $\frac{2}{9}$ hour. Who skates farther in 1 hour?

Alice's Rate   Elizabeth's Rate

Alice skates _____ miles in 1 hour.

Elizabeth skates _____ miles in 1 hour.

_____ skates farther in 1 hour.

Solve.

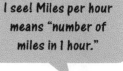

I see! Miles per hour means "number of miles in 1 hour."

6 Maurice walked 6 miles on the treadmill in $\frac{3}{2}$ hours. How many miles per hour did Maurice walk?

_____

7 On average, a person who weighs 130 pounds burns 83 calories in $\frac{1}{6}$ hour while playing basketball. At this rate, how many calories are burned in 1 hour?

_____

I can express a mixed number as an improper fraction and then write it as part of a complex fraction.

DISCUSS

Determine the Rate

Rachel wants to find the best unit price for potatoes at a grocery store. She sees a 10-pound bag for $5.90, a 5-pound bag for $2.75, and a $1\frac{1}{2}$-pound bag for $0.99.

How can Rachel find the price per pound?

Which bag has the least unit price?

What is the unit price for this bag?

PROBLEM SOLVING

CHANGING THE PACE

READ

Gabby has 5 weeks to read a novel. She reads 15 pages of a novel in $\frac{3}{7}$ week. At this rate, will Gabby read the 200-page book in time?

PLAN

• What is the problem asking you to find?

    whether Gabby can read _____ pages in _____ weeks

• What do you need to know to solve the problem?

    Gabby reads _____ pages in _____ week.

• How can you solve the problem?

    Find the unit rate. Then multiply the unit rate by _____ weeks. Compare the number to 200 pages.

SOLVE

Write the rate as a complex fraction.

$$\frac{\boxed{15}}{\frac{\boxed{3}}{\boxed{7}}}$$

Write the complex fraction as a division problem. Then rewrite as multiplication.

$$\frac{15}{\frac{3}{7}} = \underline{\hspace{1cm}} \div \underline{\hspace{1cm}} = \underline{\hspace{1cm}} \times \underline{\hspace{1cm}}$$

Multiply and simplify.

$$= \underline{\hspace{1cm}} = \underline{\hspace{1cm}} \text{ pages per week}$$

Find the number of pages she can read in 5 weeks.

$$\underline{\hspace{1cm}} \times \underline{\hspace{1cm}} = \underline{\hspace{1cm}} \text{ pages}$$

CHECK

Multiply the unit rate you found by $\frac{3}{7}$ week.

$$\frac{\boxed{} \text{ pages}}{1 \text{ week}} \times \frac{3}{7} = \underline{\hspace{1cm}} = \underline{\hspace{1cm}} \text{ pages}$$

The number of pages should be 15 with this rate.

Will Gabby finish the 200-page book in time? _____

PRACTICE

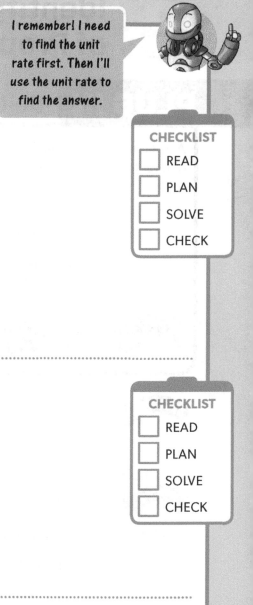

I remember! I need to find the unit rate first. Then I'll use the unit rate to find the answer.

Use the problem-solving steps to help you.

1 Marita sold 54 cups of lemonade in $\frac{1}{2}$ hour. Jennifer sold 49 cups of fruit punch in $\frac{1}{3}$ hour. Which girl sold more drinks per hour?

CHECKLIST
- [ ] READ
- [ ] PLAN
- [ ] SOLVE
- [ ] CHECK

2 A $\frac{3}{4}$-pound box contained 36 fruit tarts. How many tarts would be in a one-pound box?

CHECKLIST
- [ ] READ
- [ ] PLAN
- [ ] SOLVE
- [ ] CHECK

3 A coach compared the scoring of four players over the season. Lorraine played in 8 games and scored 128 points. Jana played in 12 games and scored 168 points. Maggie played in 9 games and scored 135 points. Nikki played in 17 games and scored 136 points. Which player scored the greatest number of points per game?

CHECKLIST
- [ ] READ
- [ ] PLAN
- [ ] SOLVE
- [ ] CHECK

Identifying the Constant of Proportionality

PLUG IN Unit Rates as Ratios

A unit rate is a ratio comparing quantities with different units of measure to a denominator equal to 1.

11 dollars per pound

$$\text{unit rate} = \frac{\text{cost}}{1 \text{ pound}} = \frac{\$11}{1 \text{ lb}}$$

35 miles per hour

$$\text{unit rate} = \frac{\text{miles}}{1 \text{ hour}} = \frac{35 \text{ mi}}{1 \text{ hr}}$$

I get it! I can write a unit rate as a fraction that has a denominator equal to 1.

You can find a unit rate by writing an equivalent rate with a denominator equal to 1.

"Jerome can type 126 words in 3 minutes."

Rate → Unit Rate

$$\frac{126 \text{ words}}{3 \text{ min}} \div \frac{3}{3} = \frac{42 \text{ words}}{1 \text{ min}}$$

I see! Jerome can type 42 words per minute.

DISCUSS Will the denominator of a unit rate ever be zero? Explain.

A Identify unit rates.

DO Decide if each description shows a unit rate.

❶ Write each description as a rate.

❷ Is the rate a unit rate? Write *yes* or *no*.

$3.25 per pound

☐ dollars
1 lb
_____

3 miles in $1\frac{1}{2}$ hours

☐ mi
☐ hr
_____

B Find a unit rate.

DO Colton used 8 gallons of gas to drive 280 miles. How many miles per gallon did Colton get during this trip?

❶ Write the rate.

❷ Divide the numerator and denominator by the same number so that the denominator becomes 1.

❸ Write the unit rate.

280 miles
☐ gallons

☐ miles
☐ gallons
÷
☐
☐
=
☐ miles
☐ gallon

Colton got _____ miles per gallon during this trip.

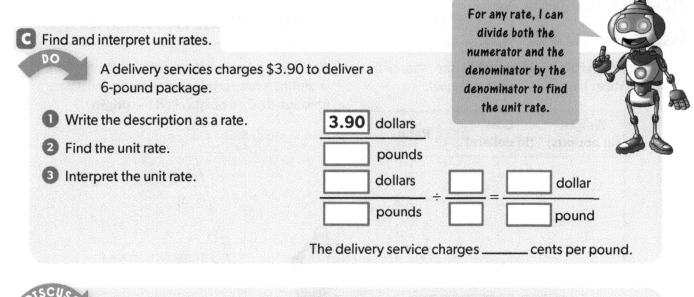

C Find and interpret unit rates.

DO

A delivery services charges $3.90 to deliver a 6-pound package.

1 Write the description as a rate.

2 Find the unit rate.

3 Interpret the unit rate.

> For any rate, I can divide both the numerator and the denominator by the denominator to find the unit rate.

$$\boxed{3.90} \text{ dollars}$$
$$\boxed{} \text{ pounds}$$

$$\frac{\boxed{} \text{ dollars}}{\boxed{} \text{ pounds}} \div \frac{\boxed{}}{\boxed{}} = \frac{\boxed{} \text{ dollar}}{\boxed{} \text{ pound}}$$

The delivery service charges _____ cents per pound.

DISCUSS

Can you find the unit rate in pounds per dollar? If so, explain what this would mean. If not, explain why.

PRACTICE

Write the description as a rate. Decide if it is a unit rate. Write *yes* or *no*.

1 10 feet per minute

$$\frac{\boxed{} \text{ feet}}{\boxed{} \text{ minute}}$$

_____

2 12 houses in 7 days

$$\frac{\boxed{} \text{ houses}}{\boxed{} \text{ days}}$$

_____

3 16 pages in 3 days

$$\frac{\boxed{} \text{ pages}}{\boxed{} \text{ days}}$$

_____

4 $8 per hour

$$\frac{\boxed{} \text{ dollars}}{\boxed{} \text{ hour}}$$

_____

Find the unit rate.

5 Jim roller-skates 12 miles in 2 hours.

_____

6 During an 8-hour shift, Sophia can make 24 sweaters.

_____

7 A 3-night stay at a cabin costs $330.

_____

8 Eliza reads 32 pages over 4 hours.

_____

POWER UP — Graphing a Proportional Relationship

In a **proportional relationship**, the ratios of the quantities being compared are equal.

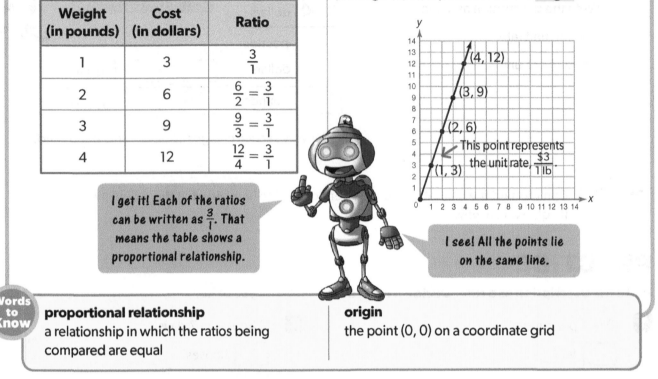

Weight (in pounds)	Cost (in dollars)	Ratio
1	3	$\frac{3}{1}$
2	6	$\frac{6}{2} = \frac{3}{1}$
3	9	$\frac{9}{3} = \frac{3}{1}$
4	12	$\frac{12}{4} = \frac{3}{1}$

I get it! Each of the ratios can be written as $\frac{3}{1}$. That means the table shows a proportional relationship.

You can use the numbers in the table to create a graph. A proportional relationship must pass through (0, 0), a point called the **origin**.

This point represents the unit rate, $\frac{\$3}{1\,\text{lb}}$.

I see! All the points lie on the same line.

Words to Know

proportional relationship
a relationship in which the ratios being compared are equal

origin
the point (0, 0) on a coordinate grid

DISCUSS

Isabella plotted four points on a graph. How can she tell if the points represent a proportional relationship?

A You can use a table to identify proportional relationships.

DO

Is this relationship proportional?

1. Write the ratio $\frac{y}{x}$ for each pair of values.

2. Write each ratio as a unit rate.

3. Find whether the ratios have the same unit rate. Determine if the relationship is proportional.

x	y	Ratio $\left(\frac{y}{x}\right)$
1	5	$\frac{5}{1}$
2	10	$\frac{10}{2} = \text{—}$
3	15	$\text{—} = \text{—}$
4	20	$\text{—} = \text{—}$
5	25	$\text{—} = \text{—}$

Is this relationship proportional? _____

I get it! In a proportional relationship, the value of y at the point (1, y) is the unit rate.

B You can graph points to identify a proportional relationship.

DO   Graph the points in this table. Is the relationship proportional? What is the unit rate?

1 Plot each point on the coordinate grid.

2 Determine if the graph shows a proportional relationship.

3 Find the unit rate.

x	y
1	4
2	8
3	12
4	16
5	20
6	24
7	28

Do the points form a line? _____

Does this line pass through the origin? _____

Is this relationship proportional? _____

When x = 1, what is the value of y? _____

Write this as an ordered pair. _____

What is the unit rate? _____

DISCUSS   Mia plotted points, including (1, 6), that form a straight line through the origin. She says the unit rate is 6. Do you agree? Explain.

PRACTICE

Graph the table of data. Is the relationship proportional? What is the unit rate?

1

x	y
1	8
2	16
3	24
4	32
5	40
6	48

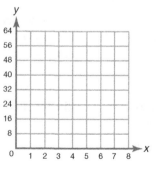

_____

_____

READY TO GO | Identifying the Constant of Proportionality

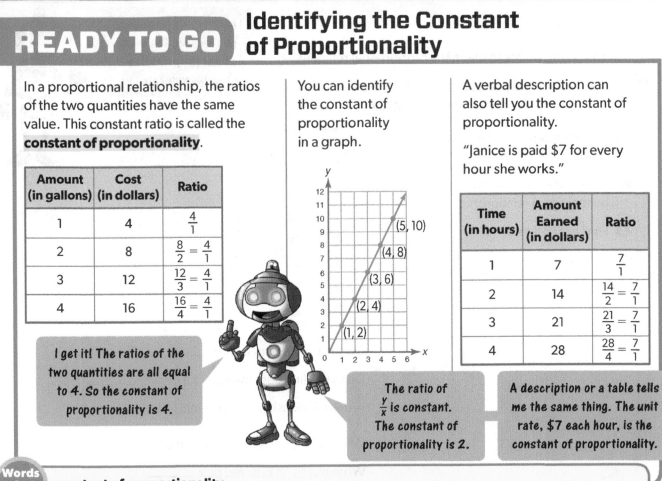

In a proportional relationship, the ratios of the two quantities have the same value. This constant ratio is called the **constant of proportionality**.

Amount (in gallons)	Cost (in dollars)	Ratio
1	4	$\frac{4}{1}$
2	8	$\frac{8}{2} = \frac{4}{1}$
3	12	$\frac{12}{3} = \frac{4}{1}$
4	16	$\frac{16}{4} = \frac{4}{1}$

I get it! The ratios of the two quantities are all equal to 4. So the constant of proportionality is 4.

You can identify the constant of proportionality in a graph.

The ratio of $\frac{y}{x}$ is constant. The constant of proportionality is 2.

A verbal description can also tell you the constant of proportionality.

"Janice is paid $7 for every hour she works."

Time (in hours)	Amount Earned (in dollars)	Ratio
1	7	$\frac{7}{1}$
2	14	$\frac{14}{2} = \frac{7}{1}$
3	21	$\frac{21}{3} = \frac{7}{1}$
4	28	$\frac{28}{4} = \frac{7}{1}$

A description or a table tells me the same thing. The unit rate, $7 each hour, is the constant of proportionality.

Words to Know

constant of proportionality
the constant ratio between two quantities in a proportional relationship

DISCUSS Kylee says that the equation $y = 7x$ represents a proportional relationship. Do you agree? Explain.

LESSON LINK

PLUG IN

A unit rate is a ratio that compares one quantity to 1 unit of another.

Rate → Unit Rate

$$\frac{14 \text{ dollars}}{7 \text{ pounds}} \div \frac{7}{7} = \frac{2 \text{ dollars}}{1 \text{ pound}}$$

The unit rate is $2 per pound.

POWER UP

In a proportional relationship, the ratios of the quantities compared are the same.

Weight (in pounds)	Cost (in dollars)	Ratio
1	2	$\frac{2}{1}$
2	4	$\frac{4}{2} = \frac{2}{1}$
3	6	$\frac{6}{3} = \frac{2}{1}$
4	8	$\frac{8}{4} = \frac{2}{1}$

GO!

I see! The unit rate of a proportional relationship is equal to the constant of proportionality.

WORK TOGETHER

You can find the constant of proportionality by using a table.

- Write the ratio for each pair of quantities.

- Write each ratio as a unit rate.

- The constant unit rate is equal to the constant of proportionality.

- The constant of proportionality is 5.

Length of Bike Ride (in hours)	Distance Traveled (in miles)	Ratio $\left(\frac{mi}{h}\right)$
1	5	$\frac{5}{1}$
2	10	$\frac{10}{2} = \frac{5}{1}$
3	15	$\frac{15}{3} = \frac{5}{1}$
4	20	$\frac{20}{4} = \frac{5}{1}$
5	25	$\frac{25}{5} = \frac{5}{1}$

I get it! I can find the constant of proportionality from a table, a graph, or a description.

A You can use a graph to find the constant of proportionality.

DO Find the constant of proportionality.

❶ Create a table showing the data points from the graph.

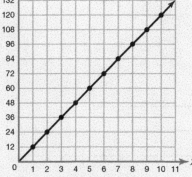

x	y	Ratio $\left(\frac{y}{x}\right)$
1		
2		
3		
4		
5		

x	y	Ratio $\left(\frac{y}{x}\right)$
6		
7		
8		
9		
10		

❷ Write the ratio, $\frac{y}{x}$, for each coordinate pair.

❸ Write each ratio as a unit rate.

❹ The constant of proportionality is equal to the constant ratio.

The constant of proportionality is _____.

DISCUSS Dylan is given the ordered pair (5, 15). He decides that the quantities in the ordered pair form a proportional relationship with a constant of proportionality of 3. Does Dylan have enough information to make this conclusion? Explain.

PRACTICE

Use the graph to determine if the relationship is proportional. Write *proportional* or *not proportional*. If the relationship is proportional, find the constant of proportionality.

1

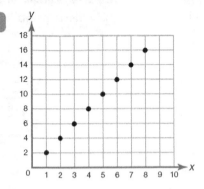

The relationship between these two quantities is _____.

What is the constant of proportionality? Explain. _____

_____

2

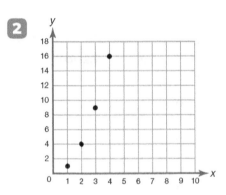

The relationship between these two quantities is _____.

What is the constant of proportionality? Explain. _____

_____

3

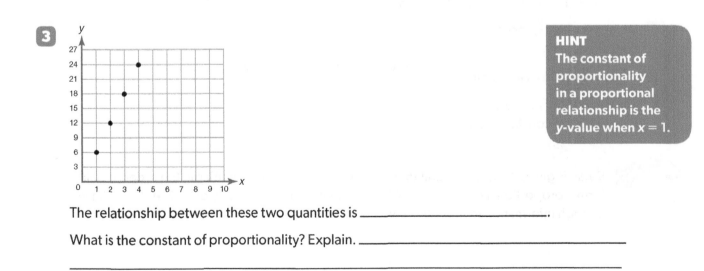

The relationship between these two quantities is _____.

What is the constant of proportionality? Explain. _____

_____

Explain why the relationship shown on the graph is not proportional.

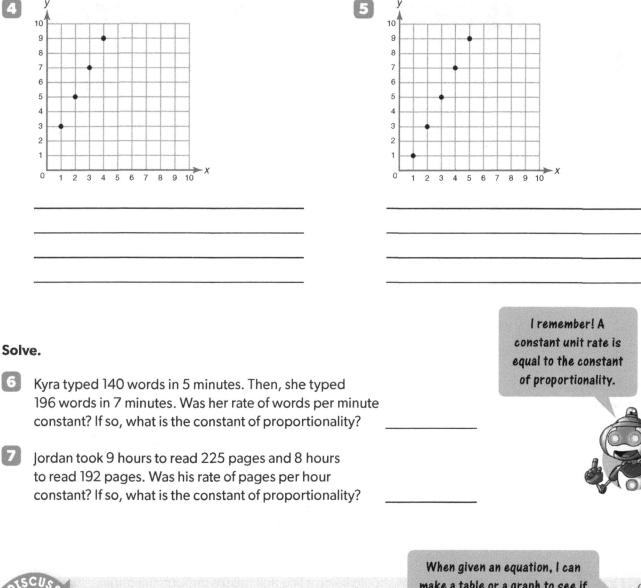

_____

_____

_____

_____

Solve.

6 Kyra typed 140 words in 5 minutes. Then, she typed 196 words in 7 minutes. Was her rate of words per minute constant? If so, what is the constant of proportionality? _____

7 Jordan took 9 hours to read 225 pages and 8 hours to read 192 pages. Was his rate of pages per hour constant? If so, what is the constant of proportionality? _____

> I remember! A constant unit rate is equal to the constant of proportionality.

> When given an equation, I can make a table or a graph to see if the relationship is proportional.

DISCUSS

Analyze

Jackson says that $y = 4x$ and $y = 4x + 2$ represent proportional relationships that have a constant of proportionality of 4. Do you agree? Explain.

PROBLEM SOLVING

Earnings State

CHECKING THE PAYCHECK

READ

Brandi read the chart to find the number of hours she worked and the amount she earned in past paychecks. Find how much Brandi earned per hour.

Time (in hours)	Amount Earned (in dollars)
2	22
4	44
6	66
8	88
10	110

PLAN

• What is the problem asking you to find?

the _____ of dollars earned to hours worked

• What do you need to know to solve the problem?

You need to know the number of hours she worked and the amount she earned. You need to find whether or not the relationship is proportional.

• How will you find the answer?

You will find the _____ of dollars to hours.

SOLVE

Write the ratios for each pair of data. Then, write each ratio as a unit rate.

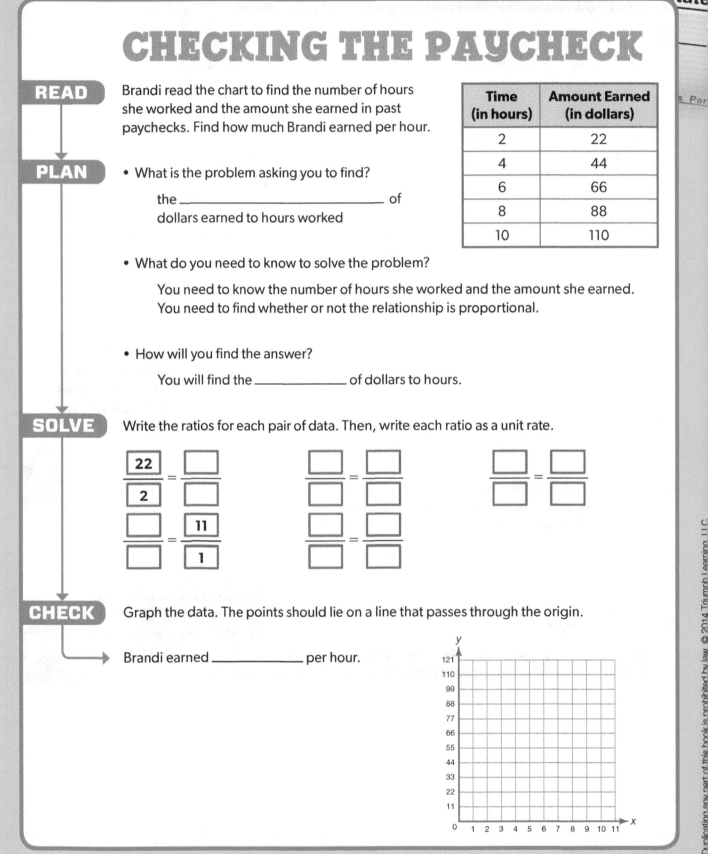

$$\frac{22}{2} = \frac{\boxed{}}{\boxed{}}$$

$$\frac{\boxed{}}{\boxed{}} = \frac{11}{1}$$

$$\frac{\boxed{}}{\boxed{}} = \frac{\boxed{}}{\boxed{}}$$

$$\frac{\boxed{}}{\boxed{}} = \frac{\boxed{}}{\boxed{}}$$

$$\frac{\boxed{}}{\boxed{}} = \frac{\boxed{}}{\boxed{}}$$

CHECK

Graph the data. The points should lie on a line that passes through the origin.

Brandi earned _____ per hour.

Rates that do not form a proportional relationship do not have a constant of proportionality.

PRACTICE

Use the problem-solving steps to help you.

1 Cassandra has a leaky roof. She places a bucket on the floor below the leak. After 2 hours, there are 26 teaspoons of water in the bowl. After 7 hours, there are 91 teaspoons of water in the bowl. Is the rate of teaspoons per hour constant? What is the constant of proportionality?

CHECKLIST
- [ ] READ
- [ ] PLAN
- [ ] SOLVE
- [ ] CHECK

2 Sierra is downloading songs. In 9 minutes, she downloads 18 songs. In 18 minutes, she downloads 36 songs. Is the rate of downloads per minute constant? What is the constant of proportionality?

CHECKLIST
- [ ] READ
- [ ] PLAN
- [ ] SOLVE
- [ ] CHECK

3 Derek is training for a long bicycle race. He bikes 105 miles in 7 days. A few weeks later, he bikes 120 miles in 10 days. Is the rate of miles per day constant? Explain your answer.

CHECKLIST
- [ ] READ
- [ ] PLAN
- [ ] SOLVE
- [ ] CHECK

Solving Real-World Problems with Ratios and Percents

PLUG IN — Writing Equivalent Forms: Fraction/Decimal/Percent

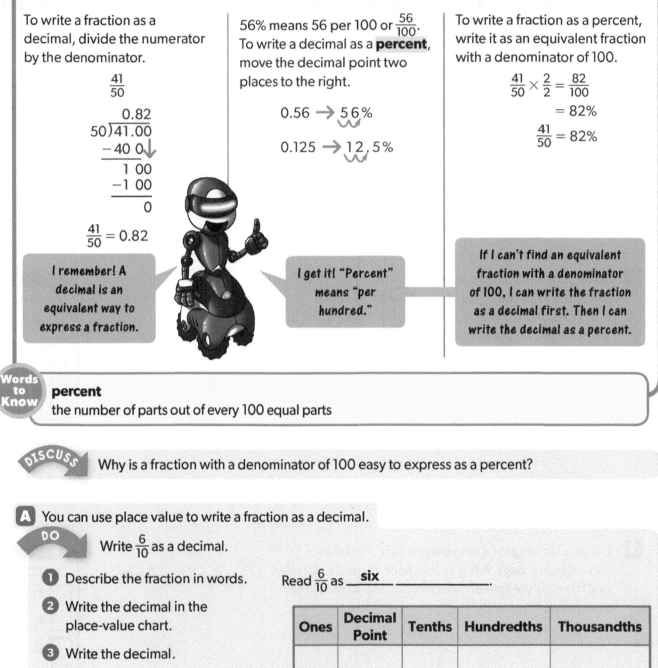

To write a fraction as a decimal, divide the numerator by the denominator.

$$\frac{41}{50}$$

$$\begin{array}{r} 0.82 \\ 50\overline{)41.00} \\ -40\ 0\downarrow \\ \hline 1\ 00 \\ -1\ 00 \\ \hline 0 \end{array}$$

$$\frac{41}{50} = 0.82$$

I remember! A decimal is an equivalent way to express a fraction.

56% means 56 per 100 or $\frac{56}{100}$. To write a decimal as a **percent**, move the decimal point two places to the right.

$0.56 \rightarrow 56\%$

$0.125 \rightarrow 12.5\%$

I get it! "Percent" means "per hundred."

To write a fraction as a percent, write it as an equivalent fraction with a denominator of 100.

$$\frac{41}{50} \times \frac{2}{2} = \frac{82}{100}$$
$$= 82\%$$
$$\frac{41}{50} = 82\%$$

If I can't find an equivalent fraction with a denominator of 100, I can write the fraction as a decimal first. Then I can write the decimal as a percent.

Words to Know

percent
the number of parts out of every 100 equal parts

DISCUSS Why is a fraction with a denominator of 100 easy to express as a percent?

A You can use place value to write a fraction as a decimal.

DO Write $\frac{6}{10}$ as a decimal.

❶ Describe the fraction in words.

❷ Write the decimal in the place-value chart.

❸ Write the decimal.

Read $\frac{6}{10}$ as ___**six**_____.

Ones	Decimal Point	Tenths	Hundredths	Thousandths

$\frac{6}{10} = $ _____

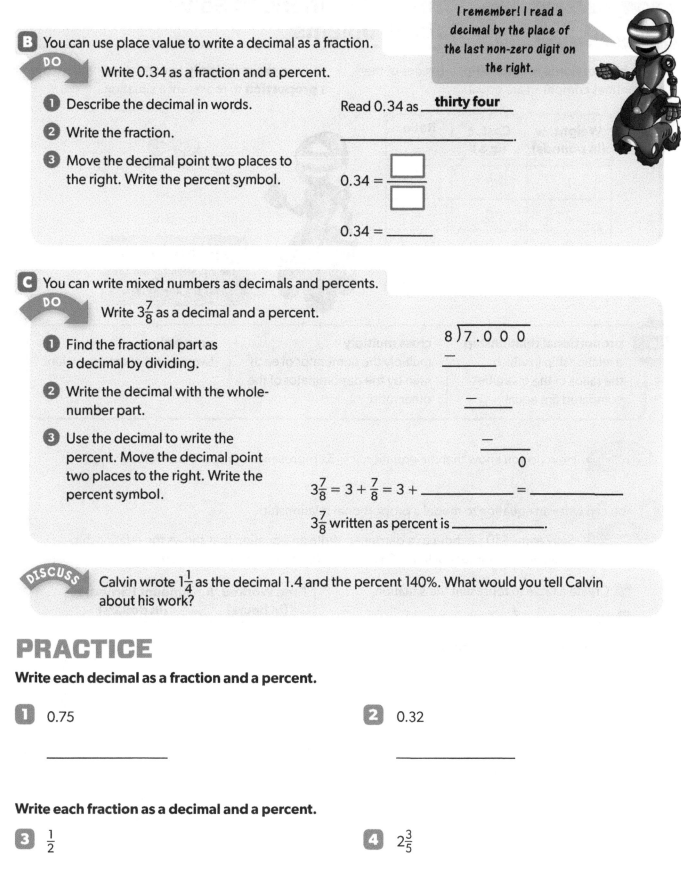

B You can use place value to write a decimal as a fraction.

I remember! I read a decimal by the place of the last non-zero digit on the right.

DO Write 0.34 as a fraction and a percent.

1 Describe the decimal in words.

Read 0.34 as ___thirty four___

2 Write the fraction.

_____.

3 Move the decimal point two places to the right. Write the percent symbol.

$0.34 = \dfrac{\boxed{}}{\boxed{}}$

$0.34 =$ _____

C You can write mixed numbers as decimals and percents.

DO Write $3\frac{7}{8}$ as a decimal and a percent.

1 Find the fractional part as a decimal by dividing.

2 Write the decimal with the whole-number part.

3 Use the decimal to write the percent. Move the decimal point two places to the right. Write the percent symbol.

$$8\overline{)7.000}$$

$3\frac{7}{8} = 3 + \frac{7}{8} = 3 +$ _____ $=$ _____

$3\frac{7}{8}$ written as percent is _____.

DISCUSS Calvin wrote $1\frac{1}{4}$ as the decimal 1.4 and the percent 140%. What would you tell Calvin about his work?

PRACTICE

Write each decimal as a fraction and a percent.

1 0.75

2 0.32

_____

_____

Write each fraction as a decimal and a percent.

3 $\frac{1}{2}$

4 $2\frac{3}{5}$

_____

_____

Writing Equations to Solve Ratio Problems

In a **proportional relationship**, the ratios of the quantities compared are equal.

Weight, w (in pounds)	Cost, c (in $)	Ratio $\left(\frac{c}{w}\right)$
1	3	$\frac{3}{1}$
2	6	$\frac{6}{2} = \frac{3}{1}$
3	9	$\frac{9}{3} = \frac{3}{1}$
4	12	$\frac{12}{4} = \frac{3}{1}$

You can **cross multiply** to write an equation from a **proportion** to represent a situation.

$$\frac{c}{w} = \frac{3}{1}$$

$$\frac{c}{w} \bowtie \frac{3}{1}$$

$$1c = 3w$$

$$c = 3w$$

I see! Now I can use the equation to find the cost for any weight.

Words to Know

proportional relationship a relationship in which the ratios of the quantities compared are equal	**cross multiply** multiply the numerator of each ratio by the denominator of the other ratio	**proportion** two ratios that are equivalent

DISCUSS How do you know that the equation $y = 5x$ represents a proportional relationship?

A You can write an equation to model a proportional relationship.

DO Sally earns $10 per hour as a gardener. Write an equation that shows the relationship between the number of hours Sally works, h, and the amount she earns, d.

❶ Create a table to represent the situation.

❷ Write the ratio $\frac{d}{h}$.

❸ Cross multiply to write the equation.

Time Worked, h (in hours)	Amount Earned, d (in dollars)
1	
2	
3	
4	

$$\frac{d}{h} = \frac{\square}{\square}$$

$$d = \underline{\hspace{2cm}}$$

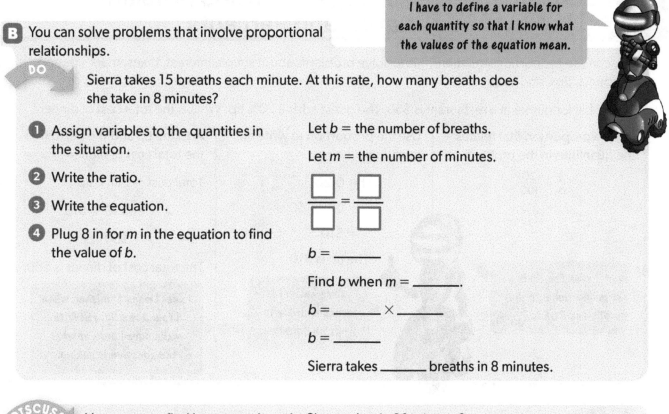

B You can solve problems that involve proportional relationships.

> I have to define a variable for each quantity so that I know what the values of the equation mean.

DO

Sierra takes 15 breaths each minute. At this rate, how many breaths does she take in 8 minutes?

❶ Assign variables to the quantities in the situation.

❷ Write the ratio.

❸ Write the equation.

❹ Plug 8 in for *m* in the equation to find the value of *b*.

Let *b* = the number of breaths.

Let *m* = the number of minutes.

$$\frac{\square}{\square} = \frac{\square}{\square}$$

b = _____

Find *b* when *m* = _____.

b = _____ × _____

b = _____

Sierra takes _____ breaths in 8 minutes.

DISCUSS   How can you find how many breaths Sierra takes in 20 minutes?

PRACTICE

Write an equation and solve.

❶ A type of bear can run at a rate of 21 miles per hour. At this rate, how far could it run in 3 hours?

_____

❷ Henry has piano lessons each week. Each lesson costs $45. How many lessons can Henry take for $540?

_____

❸ Membership for an online game service costs $25 for 2 years. At this rate, what is the cost of membership for 5 years?

_____

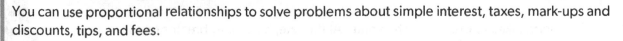

READY TO GO | Solving Real-World Problems with Ratios and Percents

You can use proportional relationships to solve problems about simple interest, taxes, mark-ups and discounts, tips, and fees.

The bill for dinner at a restaurant is $50. The guest adds a 20% tip. What is the total cost of dinner?

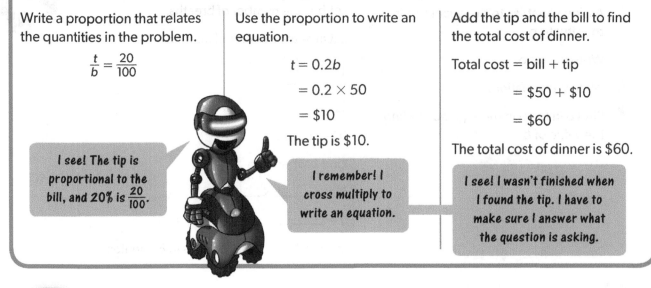

Write a proportion that relates the quantities in the problem.

$$\frac{t}{b} = \frac{20}{100}$$

I see! The tip is proportional to the bill, and 20% is $\frac{20}{100}$.

Use the proportion to write an equation.

$$t = 0.2b$$
$$= 0.2 \times 50$$
$$= \$10$$

The tip is $10.

I remember! I cross multiply to write an equation.

Add the tip and the bill to find the total cost of dinner.

$$\text{Total cost} = \text{bill} + \text{tip}$$
$$= \$50 + \$10$$
$$= \$60$$

The total cost of dinner is $60.

I see! I wasn't finished when I found the tip. I have to make sure I answer what the question is asking.

DISCUSS Why do you know you can write a proportional relationship using the tip and the bill?

LESSON LINK

PLUG IN

You can write equivalent forms of percents, decimals, and fractions.

$$50\% = 0.5 = \frac{1}{2}$$

POWER UP

You can write proportional relationships and solve problems.

$$\frac{t}{1} = \frac{20}{4}$$
$$4t = 20$$
$$t = 5$$

GO!

I get it! I can use percents, fractions, and decimals to solve real-world problems involving proportional relationships.

WORK TOGETHER

You can write an equation to solve ratio and percent problems.

- The equation $I = 0.03b$ represents the interest.
- The interest earned in the first month is $15.
- Add the interest to find the value of the account after one month.
- The value of the account after one month is $515.
- The interest earned in the second month is $15.45.
- Add the interest to find the value of the account after two months.
- The value of the account after two months is $530.45.

I need to convert the percent to a decimal to write the equation.

Julio starts a savings account with $500. The account earns 3% simple interest each month. What will be the value of the account after two months?

Let I = interest earned. Let b = account balance.

$I = 0.03b$

$I = 0.03 \times b = 0.03 \times 500 = \$15$

First month: $500 + $15 = $515.

$I = 0.03 \times b = 0.03 \times 515 = \$15.45$

Second month: $515 + $15.45 = $530.45.

A Use percents to calculate taxes.

DO

Sergei buys a $200 airplane ticket. He also pays a 7% travel tax on the ticket price and a 6% baggage tax on the ticket price. What is the total amount he paid for the ticket?

1 Write an equation to find the travel tax.

2 Write an equation to find the baggage tax.

3 Add both taxes to the original price to find the total amount paid.

4 Write the total amount.

Let t = travel tax amount.

$t = \underline{\hspace{1cm}} \times 200 = \underline{\hspace{1cm}}$

The travel tax is $\underline{\hspace{1cm}}.

Let b = baggage tax amount.

$b = \underline{\hspace{1cm}} \times 200 = \underline{\hspace{1cm}}$

The baggage tax is $\underline{\hspace{1cm}}.

$200 + $\underline{\hspace{1cm}} + $\underline{\hspace{1cm}} = $\underline{\hspace{1cm}}

The total amount paid is $\underline{\hspace{1cm}}.

DISCUSS

Yolanda solves the problem by writing the expression $200 \times 0.07 \times 0.06$. Would this method work for finding the travel tax and baggage tax? If not, what value does it find? Explain.

PRACTICE

Work through each step to solve the problem.

1 A store manager buys a video game for $15. He marks up the price by 20% to sell it in his store. What is the price of the game in his store?

Find the markup.

$m = $ __**0.2**__ $\times$ \$15 = \$_____

Find the cost of the game after the markup.

original cost + markup = store price

\$_____ + \$_____ = \$_____

> **HINT**
> A markup is an amount added to the cost of an item before it is sold.

2 Mike's savings account earns 1% simple interest every week. If he starts his account with $600, what will be the balance in the account after two weeks?

Start:	$600
First week's interest:	\$__**600**__ $\times$ __**0.01**__ = \$_____
Account balance after 1 week:	\$_____ + \$_____ = \$_____
Second week's interest:	\$_____ $\times$ _____ = \$_____
Account balance after 2 weeks:	\$_____ + \$_____ = \$_____

> **REMEMBER**
> The interest earned in the first week becomes part of the account for the second week.

3 A DVD is on sale for 60% of its original price. A tax of 8% is added to the sale price. If the original price was $20, what is the cost of the DVD with tax?

Find the sale price.

60% of $20 is the sale price.

_____ $\times$ \$_____ = \$_____

Find the tax.

\$_____ $\times$ _____ = \$_____

Find the total cost.

\$_____ + \$_____ = \$_____

4 Layla buys a pair of sneakers that are 50% off. A tax of 6% is added to the sale price. If the original price was $45, how much did Layla pay for the sneakers, including tax?

Find the sale price.

50% of $45 is the sale price.

_____ $\times$ \$_____ = \$_____

Find the tax.

\$_____ $\times$ _____ = \$_____

Find the total cost.

\$_____ + \$_____ = \$_____

Use percents to solve the problem.

5 Rodrigo's taxi fare is $9. A gasoline tax of 2% of the fare is added to the fare.
He gives the driver 20% of the fare as a tip. How much did Rodrigo pay in all for his taxi ride?

$ _____

6 Aisha and Marisol's lunch bill is $23. Aisha adds 8% of the bill as a tip and Marisol adds 7%.
What is the total cost of their lunch?

$ _____

Solve.

A commission is a fee salespeople earn based on the value of the items they sell.

7 A car salesperson earns a 4% commission for each car he sells. He sells a car for $21,250.
How much commission does the salesperson earn? $ _____

8 Pumpkins were 20% off the week before the Harvest Festival and then another 50% off the week after.
If the original price of a pumpkin is $10, how much did it cost the week after the Harvest Festival? $ _____

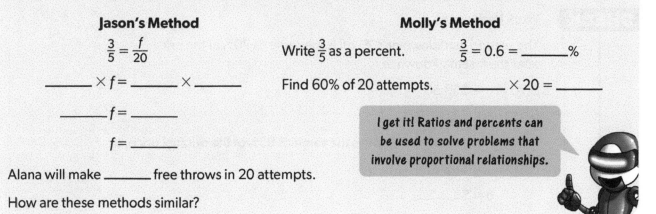

DISCUSS

See the Relationship

Two students use different methods to solve the following problem.

At basketball practice, Alana makes 3 of her last 5 free throw attempts.
If she continues at this rate, how many free throws will she make in her next 20 attempts?

Jason's Method

$$\frac{3}{5} = \frac{f}{20}$$

_____ × f = _____ × _____

_____ f = _____

f = _____

Alana will make _____ free throws in 20 attempts.

How are these methods similar?

Molly's Method

Write $\frac{3}{5}$ as a percent. $\frac{3}{5} = 0.6 =$ _____%

Find 60% of 20 attempts.   _____ × 20 = _____

I get it! Ratios and percents can be used to solve problems that involve proportional relationships.

PROBLEM SOLVING

POSTER SALE

READ

A framed movie poster originally cost $100. It has been marked down 15%, and then another 30%. If Ahmed has $60, will he be able to buy the poster?

PLAN

• What is the problem asking you to find?

Compare $60 to the final _____ of the poster.

• What do you need to know to solve the problem?

The original price of the poster is $_____.

It had been marked down _____%, then another _____%.

SOLVE

Find the amount of the first markdown, *f*.

$f = $ __**0.15**__ $\times$ _____ = _____

Find the price of the poster, *a*, after the first markdown.

$a = \$100 - $ _____ = $_____

Find the amount of the second markdown, *s*.

$s = $ __**0.30**__ $\times \$$ _____ = $_____

Find the price of the poster, *b*, after the second markdown.

$b = \$$ _____ $- \$$ _____ = $_____

Compare the value of *b* to $60.

CHECK

Work backward.

The second markdown of 30% off is the same as 70% of the price after the first markdown, *a*.

$0.70 \times a = \$59.50$

$a = \$$ _____

The first markdown of 15% off is the same as 85% of the original price, *o*.

$0.85 \times o = \$85$

$o = \$$ _____

Is the original price, *o*, $100? _____

Ahmed _____ be able to buy the poster.

PRACTICE

Use the problem-solving steps to help you.

1 Carmen buys a book that is discounted 50%. A tax of 6% is added to the sale price. The book originally cost $14. If Carmen gives the cashier $10, how much change will she get back?

CHECKLIST
- [ ] READ
- [ ] PLAN
- [ ] SOLVE
- [ ] CHECK

2 Tyrese's breakfast costs $9. A tax of 4% is added to the bill. He wants to leave 15% of the cost of the breakfast (without tax) as the tip. Find the total cost of Tyrese's breakfast with tax and tip. If he pays with a $20 bill, what will be his change?

CHECKLIST
- [ ] READ
- [ ] PLAN
- [ ] SOLVE
- [ ] CHECK

3 Gloria wants to buy a basketball jersey that originally cost $30. Last week, the price of the jersey went up 40%. This week, the jersey is on sale for 30% off. Find the price of the jersey this week.

CHECKLIST
- [ ] READ
- [ ] PLAN
- [ ] SOLVE
- [ ] CHECK

Using Proportional Relationships to Solve Multi-Step Problems

PLUG IN · Using Percents

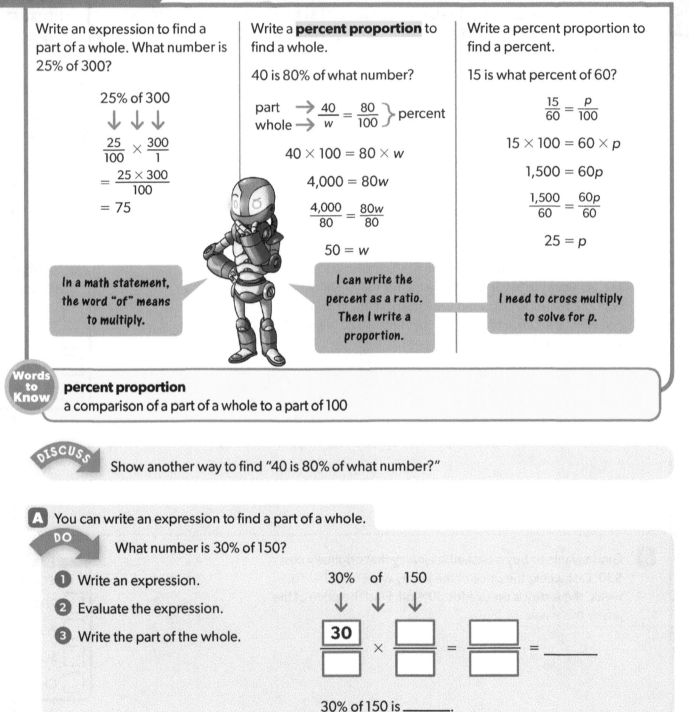

Write an expression to find a part of a whole. What number is 25% of 300?

25% of 300
↓ ↓ ↓
$\frac{25}{100} \times \frac{300}{1}$
$= \frac{25 \times 300}{100}$
$= 75$

> In a math statement, the word "of" means to multiply.

Write a **percent proportion** to find a whole.

40 is 80% of what number?

part → $\frac{40}{w} = \frac{80}{100}$ } percent
whole →

$40 \times 100 = 80 \times w$

$4,000 = 80w$

$\frac{4,000}{80} = \frac{80w}{80}$

$50 = w$

> I can write the percent as a ratio. Then I write a proportion.

Write a percent proportion to find a percent.

15 is what percent of 60?

$\frac{15}{60} = \frac{p}{100}$

$15 \times 100 = 60 \times p$

$1,500 = 60p$

$\frac{1,500}{60} = \frac{60p}{60}$

$25 = p$

> I need to cross multiply to solve for p.

Words to Know

percent proportion
a comparison of a part of a whole to a part of 100

DISCUSS

Show another way to find "40 is 80% of what number?"

A You can write an expression to find a part of a whole.

DO What number is 30% of 150?

1. Write an expression.
2. Evaluate the expression.
3. Write the part of the whole.

30%   of   150
↓   ↓   ↓

$\boxed{\frac{\boxed{30}}{\boxed{}} \times \frac{\boxed{}}{\boxed{}} = \frac{\boxed{}}{\boxed{}}} = \underline{}$

30% of 150 is _____.

I get it! I can use a percent proportion to find a part, a whole, or a percent.

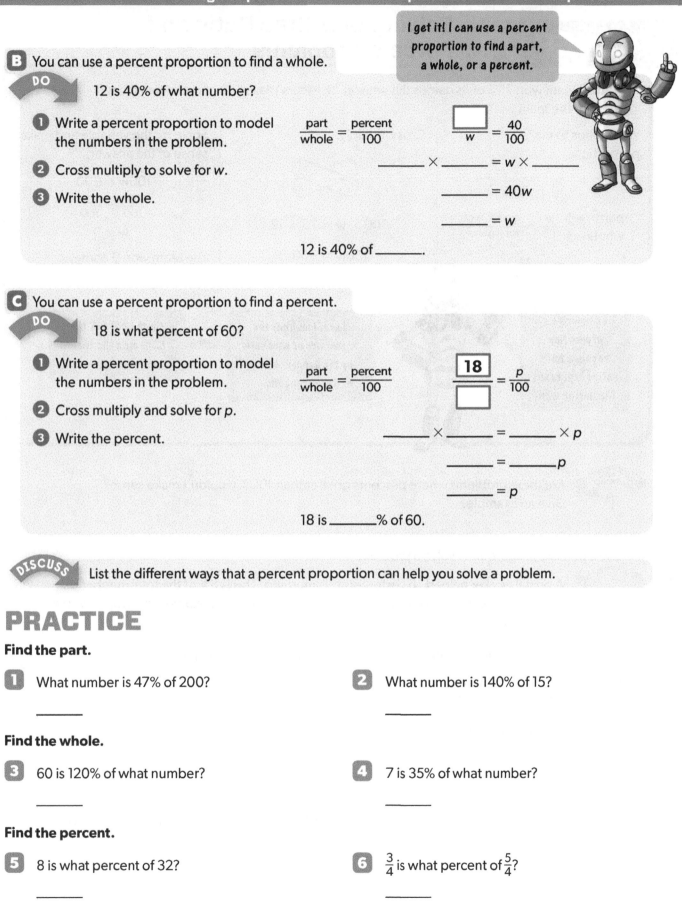

B You can use a percent proportion to find a whole.

DO 12 is 40% of what number?

1. Write a percent proportion to model the numbers in the problem.

   $\dfrac{\text{part}}{\text{whole}} = \dfrac{\text{percent}}{100}$ $\dfrac{\boxed{}}{w} = \dfrac{40}{100}$

2. Cross multiply to solve for w.

   _____ × _____ = w × _____

3. Write the whole.

   _____ = $40w$

   _____ = w

   12 is 40% of _____.

C You can use a percent proportion to find a percent.

DO 18 is what percent of 60?

1. Write a percent proportion to model the numbers in the problem.

   $\dfrac{\text{part}}{\text{whole}} = \dfrac{\text{percent}}{100}$ $\dfrac{\boxed{18}}{\boxed{}} = \dfrac{p}{100}$

2. Cross multiply and solve for p.

   _____ × _____ = _____ × p

3. Write the percent.

   _____ = _____ p

   _____ = p

   18 is _____% of 60.

DISCUSS List the different ways that a percent proportion can help you solve a problem.

PRACTICE

Find the part.

1 What number is 47% of 200?

_____

2 What number is 140% of 15?

_____

Find the whole.

3 60 is 120% of what number?

_____

4 7 is 35% of what number?

_____

Find the percent.

5 8 is what percent of 32?

_____

6 $\frac{3}{4}$ is what percent of $\frac{5}{4}$?

_____

Solving One-Step Ratio and Percent Problems

A football team won 75% of its games this season. The team played 12 games. How many games did the team win?

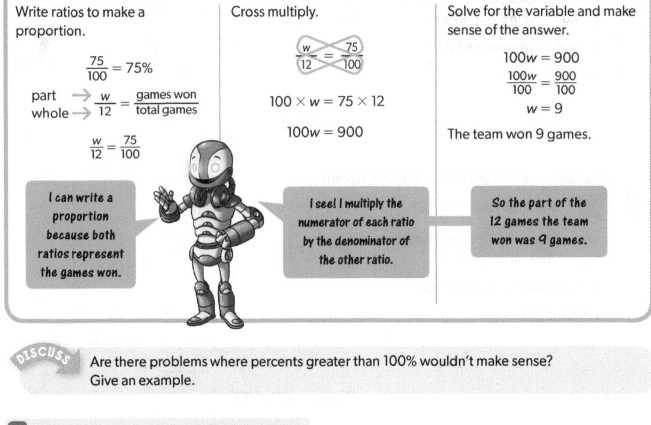

Write ratios to make a proportion.

$$\frac{75}{100} = 75\%$$

part → $\frac{w}{12}$ = $\frac{\text{games won}}{\text{total games}}$
whole →

$$\frac{w}{12} = \frac{75}{100}$$

> I can write a proportion because both ratios represent the games won.

Cross multiply.

$$\frac{w}{12} = \frac{75}{100}$$

$$100 \times w = 75 \times 12$$

$$100w = 900$$

> I see! I multiply the numerator of each ratio by the denominator of the other ratio.

Solve for the variable and make sense of the answer.

$$100w = 900$$
$$\frac{100w}{100} = \frac{900}{100}$$
$$w = 9$$

The team won 9 games.

> So the part of the 12 games the team won was 9 games.

DISCUSS Are there problems where percents greater than 100% wouldn't make sense? Give an example.

A Use a percent proportion to solve a problem.

DO

A postal worker helped 16 customers this morning. This is 8% of the total number of customers she will help today. What is the total number of customers the postal worker will help today?

❶ Decide what you need to find.

❷ Write a percent proportion to find the total number of customers, *w*.

❸ Cross multiply and solve for *w*.

____**16**____ is _____% of what number?

$$\frac{\boxed{}}{w} = \frac{\boxed{}}{100}$$

_____ × _____ = _____ × _____

_____*w* = _____

w = _____

The postal worker will help a total of _____ customers.

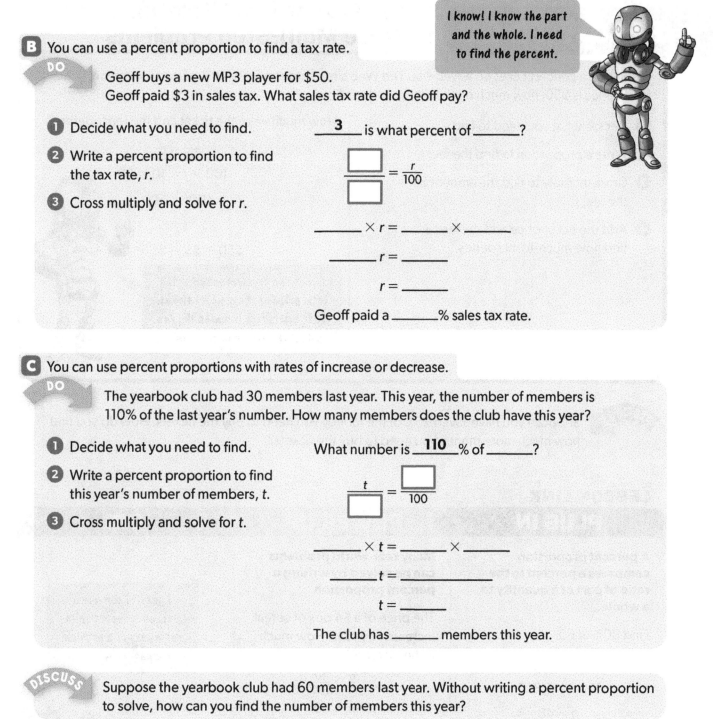

B You can use a percent proportion to find a tax rate.

> I know! I know the part and the whole. I need to find the percent.

DO

Geoff buys a new MP3 player for $50.
Geoff paid $3 in sales tax. What sales tax rate did Geoff pay?

1 Decide what you need to find.

2 Write a percent proportion to find the tax rate, r.

3 Cross multiply and solve for r.

_____**3**_____ is what percent of _____?

$$\frac{\boxed{}}{\boxed{}} = \frac{r}{100}$$

_____ × r = _____ × _____

_____ r = _____

r = _____

Geoff paid a _____% sales tax rate.

C You can use percent proportions with rates of increase or decrease.

DO

The yearbook club had 30 members last year. This year, the number of members is 110% of the last year's number. How many members does the club have this year?

1 Decide what you need to find.

2 Write a percent proportion to find this year's number of members, t.

3 Cross multiply and solve for t.

What number is _____**110**_____% of _____?

$$\frac{t}{\boxed{}} = \frac{\boxed{}}{100}$$

_____ × t = _____ × _____

_____ t = _____

t = _____

The club has _____ members this year.

DISCUSS

Suppose the yearbook club had 60 members last year. Without writing a percent proportion to solve, how can you find the number of members this year?

PRACTICE

Solve.

1 Betty received an A on 80% of her math quizzes. She took 15 math quizzes. On how many quizzes did Betty receive an A?

_____

2 A bank account pays 5% interest each year. If you start an account with $150, how much interest will you earn in one year?

_____

Using Proportional Relationships to Solve Multi-Step Problems

Toshi buys a concert ticket on a Web site. The Web site charges a fee of 10% of the ticket price. If the ticket price is $50, how much does Toshi spend in all?

① Decide what you need to find.

② Write a proportion to find the fee, f.

③ Cross multiply to find the amount of the fee, f.

④ Add the ticket price and the fee to find how much Toshi spends.

How much were the ticket and the fee together?

$$\frac{10}{100} = \frac{f}{50}$$
$$100 \times f = 10 \times 50$$
$$100f = 500$$
$$f = 5$$
$$\$50 + \$5 = \$55$$

> I see! The problem asks for the total price of the concert ticket. That total price includes the fee that the Web site charges.

DISCUSS

Suppose you have saved 75% of the money you need to buy the tickets. How do you find how much more money you need to buy the tickets?

LESSON LINK

PLUG IN	POWER UP	GO!
A percent proportion compares a percent to the ratio of part of a quantity to a whole.	Many real-world problems can be solved by writing a percent proportion.	I get it! I can use a percent proportion to solve part of a problem that has many steps!

PLUG IN

A percent proportion compares a percent to the ratio of part of a quantity to a whole.

Find 80% of 60.

$$\frac{n}{60} = \frac{80}{100}$$
$$100n = 4,800$$
$$n = 48$$

POWER UP

Many real-world problems can be solved by writing a percent proportion.

The price of a $4 box of cereal increases by 10%. How much is the increase?

$$\frac{n}{4} = \frac{10}{100}$$
$$100n = 40$$
$$n = \$0.40$$

GO!

I get it! I can use a percent proportion to solve part of a problem that has many steps!

WORK TOGETHER

You can use what you know about ratios and percents to find a percent of increase.

- The amount of change is 3 ounces.

- Write a percent proportion to find p, the percent of increase.

- The percent of increase is 50%.

A snack company increased the weight of crackers sold in each box from 6 ounces to 9 ounces. What is the percent of increase in the weight of crackers in each box?

$$9 - 6 = 3$$

$$\frac{\text{amount of change}}{\text{original amount}} = \frac{\text{percent}}{100}$$

$$\frac{3}{6} = \frac{p}{100}$$

$$6p = 300$$

$$p = 50$$

The percent of increase tells me how much more each box weighs.

A You can find a percent of decrease with ratios and percents.

DO

Alicia sent 50 text messages last month. This month, she sends 38 text messages. What is the percent of decrease in the number of text messages Alicia sent?

❶ Find the amount of change.

❷ Write an equation to find the percent of decrease, d.

❸ Calculate the percent of decrease.

_____ − _____ = _____

$$d = \frac{\text{amount of change}}{\text{original amount}}$$

$$d = \frac{\boxed{}}{\boxed{}} = \text{_____}$$

The percent of decrease is _____%.

B Percent of error can be found by using ratios and proportions.

DO

A student measures that 84 mL of rainwater has fallen. The actual amount is 80 mL of rainwater. What is his percent of error?

❶ Find the difference in the measurement and the actual value.

❷ Write a percent proportion to find the percent of error, e.

❸ Solve for e.

_____ − _____ = _____

$$\frac{\text{amount of error}}{\text{actual value}} = \frac{\text{percent}}{100}$$

$$\frac{\boxed{}}{80} = \frac{e}{100}$$

$$e = \text{_____}$$

The percent of error is _____%.

DISCUSS How do you know whether a problem is asking you to find the percent of increase or the percent of decrease?

PRACTICE

Solve. Show your work.

1 A real estate company charges a fee of 6% to sell a house. The agent gets to keep half of this fee. If an agent sells a house for $80,000, what amount does the agent get to keep?

2 Andre answered 42 questions correctly at this year's spelling bee. Last year, he answered 35 questions correctly. What is the percent increase in the number of questions he answered correctly?

> **REMEMBER**
> The percent of change ratio compares the amount of change with the original amount.

3 The regular price of a video game system is $250. It is on sale for 20% off. What is the total cost of this video game system on sale after a 6% sales tax is included?

> **HINT**
> Find the sale price first. Then add the tax.

4 Alexandra takes a measurement of 294 grams in a science class. The actual amount is 300 grams. What is the percent error of Alexandra's measurement?

5 A bank charges 8% interest per year for a loan. Roger takes out a $5,000 loan and then pays it back one year later with interest. How much does Roger pay back to the bank?

Solve.

I'll find the cost of the jeans at each store first.

6 At Store A, a pair of jeans costs $35. The same kind of jeans costs $45 at Store B. These jeans are on sale at Store A for 20% off and at Store B for 30% off. At which store will the jeans cost less?

_____

7 This year, 470 students attended the junior high school. Last year, 500 students attended the school. What is the percent of decrease in the number of students?

_____

DISCUSS

Analyze

The regular price of a pair of shoes is $50. Lin sees the shoes on sale for 10% off but notices that there is an additional 10% sales tax. She says, at the sale price and with tax, the shoes will cost the same as the regular price. Is Lin correct? Explain your response.

The discount is an amount subtracted from the regular price. The sales tax is an amount added to the discounted price.

PROBLEM SOLVING

TAXES

READ

John earns $500 each week. He pays taxes that total 20% of his earnings. If John also pays $50 in other fees, how much of his total earnings does he keep each week?

PLAN

• What is the problem asking you to find?

You need to find _____.

• What do you need to know to solve the problem?

John earns _____ each week. The percent of taxes paid is _____.

John pays _____ in other fees.

• How can you solve the problem?

Find the total amount in taxes and fees paid. Then subtract from $500.

SOLVE

Find the amount paid in taxes.

20% of $500

$$\frac{\boxed{n}}{\boxed{500}} = \frac{\boxed{20}}{\boxed{100}}$$

_____ = _____ × _____ = _____

_____ = _____

Find the total amount paid in taxes and other fees.

$\dfrac{100}{}$ + _____ = _____

Subtract the total amount paid in taxes and other fees from the total earnings.

_____ − _____ = _____

CHECK

The sum of the taxes and other fees and the amount John keeps should equal his total earnings.

Add the other fees first.

_____ + _____ = _____

Add the taxes.

_____ + _____ = _____

John keeps _____ each week.

PRACTICE

Use the problem-solving steps to help you.

1 Hector's lunch bill totals $15. He decides to leave a 20% tip. How much does he pay in all?

CHECKLIST
- [ ] READ
- [ ] PLAN
- [ ] SOLVE
- [ ] CHECK

2 Students in a science class measure the height of a bean plant. One week, the height is 2 inches. Two weeks later, the height is 3 inches. What is the percent of increase of the height of the bean plant?

CHECKLIST
- [ ] READ
- [ ] PLAN
- [ ] SOLVE
- [ ] CHECK

3 A large rock has an actual weight of 2,500 kilograms. To check her new scale, a scientist measures the rock's weight to be 2,450 kilograms. What is the scale's percent of error?

I'll find the ratio of the error in measurement to the actual weight and then write it as a percent.

CHECKLIST
- [ ] READ
- [ ] PLAN
- [ ] SOLVE
- [ ] CHECK

Adding and Subtracting Rational Numbers

PLUG IN Representing Opposite Situations

You can represent opposite situations on a number line.

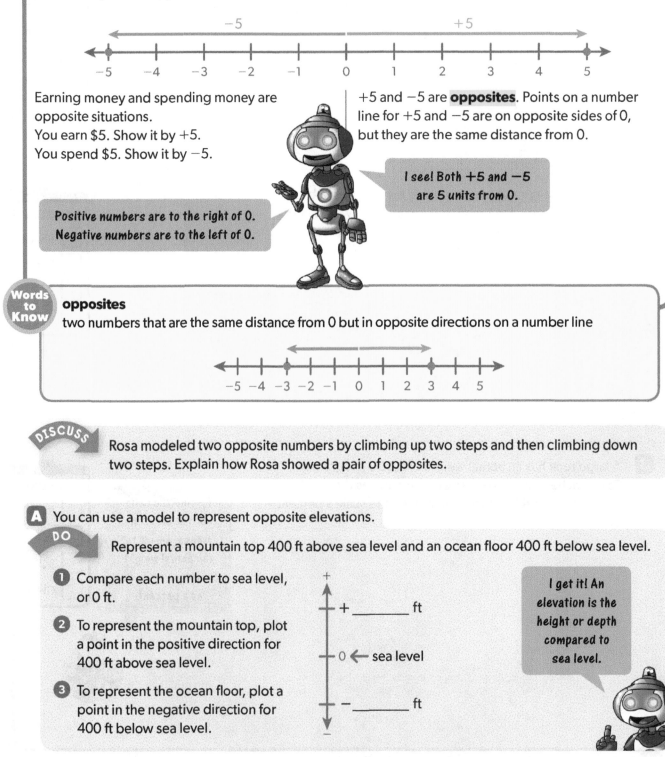

−5   +5

−5 −4 −3 −2 −1 0 1 2 3 4 5

Earning money and spending money are opposite situations.
You earn $5. Show it by +5.
You spend $5. Show it by −5.

+5 and −5 are **opposites**. Points on a number line for +5 and −5 are on opposite sides of 0, but they are the same distance from 0.

I see! Both +5 and −5 are 5 units from 0.

Positive numbers are to the right of 0.
Negative numbers are to the left of 0.

Words to Know

opposites
two numbers that are the same distance from 0 but in opposite directions on a number line

−5 −4 −3 −2 −1 0 1 2 3 4 5

DISCUSS Rosa modeled two opposite numbers by climbing up two steps and then climbing down two steps. Explain how Rosa showed a pair of opposites.

A You can use a model to represent opposite elevations.

DO Represent a mountain top 400 ft above sea level and an ocean floor 400 ft below sea level.

1 Compare each number to sea level, or 0 ft.

2 To represent the mountain top, plot a point in the positive direction for 400 ft above sea level.

3 To represent the ocean floor, plot a point in the negative direction for 400 ft below sea level.

+ _____ ft

0 ← sea level

− _____ ft

I get it! An elevation is the height or depth compared to sea level.

A thermometer is similar to a vertical number line.

B You can use a model to represent opposite temperatures.

DO Represent 20°C above freezing at noon and 20°C below freezing at midnight.

1 Compare each number to freezing, or 0°C.

2 Label the temperature at noon at 20°C above freezing.

3 Label the temperature at midnight at 20°C below freezing.

4 Explain the meaning of each number.

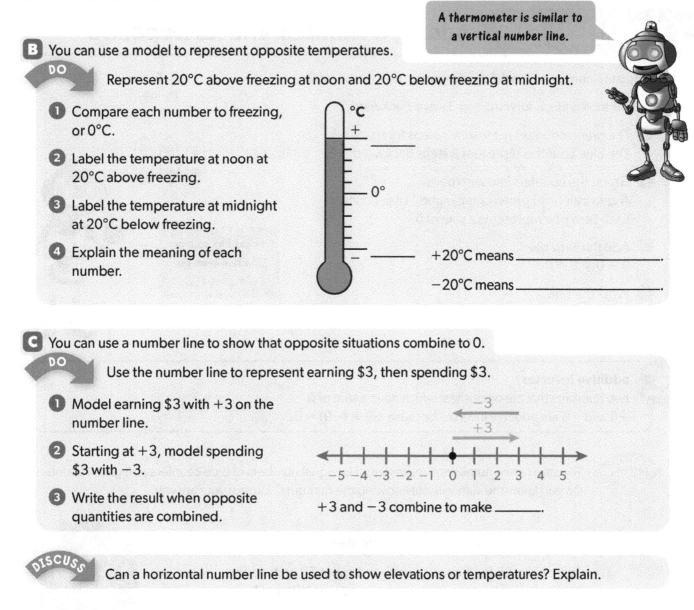

°C

+ _____

0°

+20°C means _____.

−20°C means _____.

C You can use a number line to show that opposite situations combine to 0.

DO Use the number line to represent earning $3, then spending $3.

1 Model earning $3 with +3 on the number line.

2 Starting at +3, model spending $3 with −3.

3 Write the result when opposite quantities are combined.

−3

+3

−5 −4 −3 −2 −1 0 1 2 3 4 5

+3 and −3 combine to make _____.

DISCUSS Can a horizontal number line be used to show elevations or temperatures? Explain.

PRACTICE

Plot on the number line to represent opposites.

1 8 ft above the ground and 8 ft below the ground

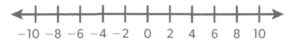

−10 −8 −6 −4 −2 0 2 4 6 8 10

2 A beetle started from the ground and crawled 4 in. up a stem. It then climbed 4 in. back down.

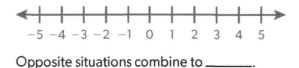

−5 −4 −3 −2 −1 0 1 2 3 4 5

Opposite situations combine to _____.

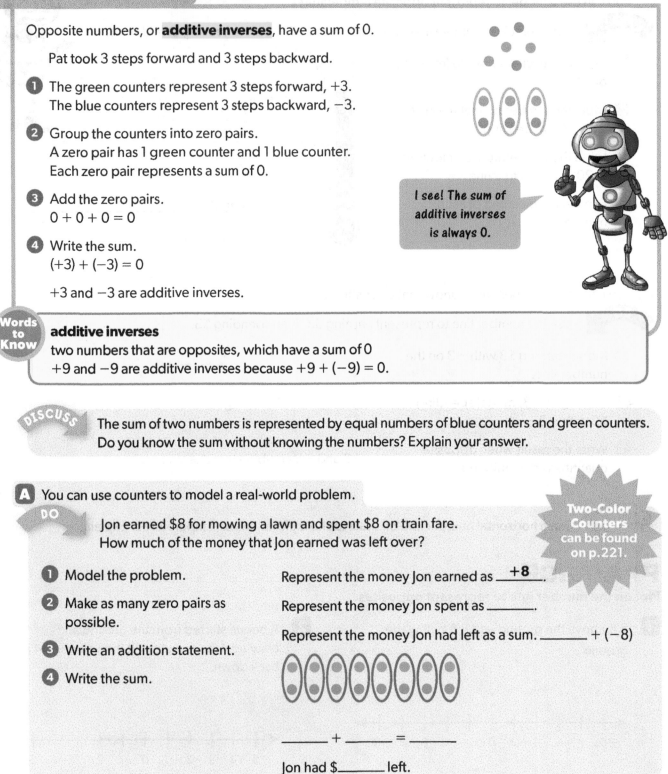

POWER UP Adding a Number and its Opposite

Opposite numbers, or **additive inverses**, have a sum of 0.

Pat took 3 steps forward and 3 steps backward.

1 The green counters represent 3 steps forward, +3.
The blue counters represent 3 steps backward, −3.

2 Group the counters into zero pairs.
A zero pair has 1 green counter and 1 blue counter.
Each zero pair represents a sum of 0.

3 Add the zero pairs.
$0 + 0 + 0 = 0$

4 Write the sum.
$(+3) + (−3) = 0$

+3 and −3 are additive inverses.

I see! The sum of additive inverses is always 0.

Words to Know

additive inverses
two numbers that are opposites, which have a sum of 0
+9 and −9 are additive inverses because $+9 + (−9) = 0$.

DISCUSS The sum of two numbers is represented by equal numbers of blue counters and green counters.
Do you know the sum without knowing the numbers? Explain your answer.

A You can use counters to model a real-world problem.

DO Jon earned $8 for mowing a lawn and spent $8 on train fare.
How much of the money that Jon earned was left over?

Two-Color Counters can be found on p. 221.

1 Model the problem.

2 Make as many zero pairs as possible.

3 Write an addition statement.

4 Write the sum.

Represent the money Jon earned as ___+8___.

Represent the money Jon spent as _____.

Represent the money Jon had left as a sum. _____ + (−8)

_____ + _____ = _____

Jon had $_____ left.

I see! A negative value for depth means a distance below sea level.

B You can use a number line to model a real-world problem.

DO

A swimmer dove 15 ft under the water. She then dove down another 13 ft. What was the swimmer's final depth?

❶ Model the problem.

Represent the first part of the dive as ___−15___.

❷ Start the first arrow at 0. Start the second arrow where the first arrow ends. Plot a point where the second arrow ends.

Represent the second part of the dive as ___−13___.

Represent the final depth as a sum. _____ + (−13)

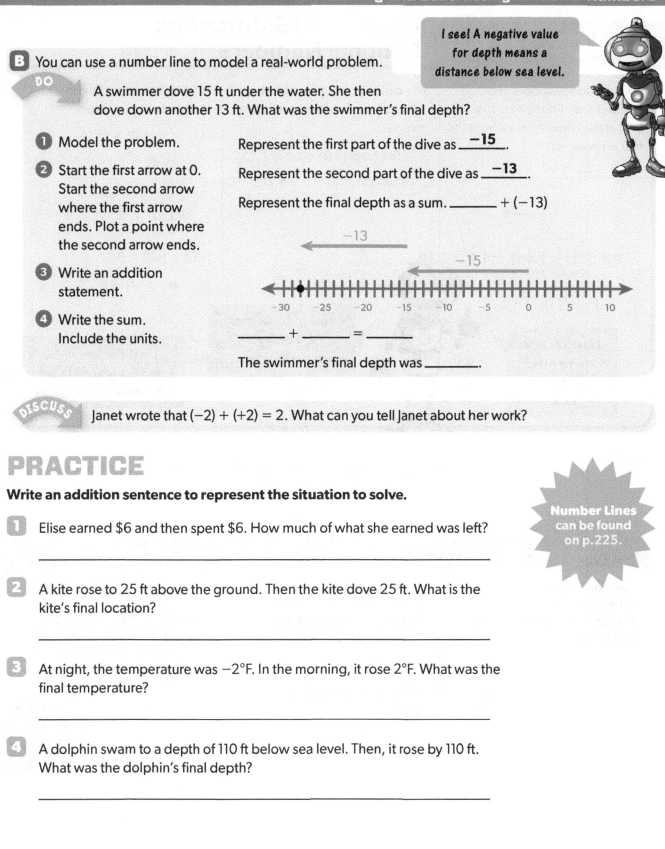

❸ Write an addition statement.

❹ Write the sum. Include the units.

_____ + _____ = _____

The swimmer's final depth was _____.

DISCUSS

Janet wrote that (−2) + (+2) = 2. What can you tell Janet about her work?

PRACTICE

Write an addition sentence to represent the situation to solve.

Number Lines can be found on p. 225.

❶ Elise earned $6 and then spent $6. How much of what she earned was left?

_____

❷ A kite rose to 25 ft above the ground. Then the kite dove 25 ft. What is the kite's final location?

_____

❸ At night, the temperature was −2°F. In the morning, it rose 2°F. What was the final temperature?

_____

❹ A dolphin swam to a depth of 110 ft below sea level. Then, it rose by 110 ft. What was the dolphin's final depth?

_____

Adding and Subtracting Rational Numbers

You can add numbers on a number line. Start one arrow at 0. Start the next arrow where the first arrow ends.

Add $(+3) + (+2)$.

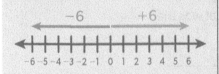

$(+3) + (+2) = 5$

> I see! The sum is where the second arrow ends.

You can subtract a number by adding its opposite, or additive inverse.

Subtract $(+6) - (-2)$.

The opposite of -2 is 2.

$(+6) - (-2) = (+6) + (+2)$

> I get it! To subtract -2, I think of its additive inverse, 2, and then add.

Add on a number line to complete the problem.

$(+6) + (+2)$

$(+6) + (+2) = 8$

So, $+6 - (-2) = 8$

> I see! The sum of $+6$ and $+2$ is equal to the difference of $+6$ and -2!

DISCUSS On a number line, how would adding a number look different from adding its opposite?

LESSON LINK

PLUG IN

You can represent opposite situations with numbers, descriptions, or arrows on number lines.

POWER UP

You can show on a number line or with counters that the sum of a number and its opposite is always 0.

$(-6) + (+6) = 0$

-6 and $+6$ are additive inverses.

GO!

> I get it! I can use what I've learned about opposites and number lines to add or subtract rational numbers.

WORK TOGETHER

You can use Number Lines to find the difference between rational numbers.

- Write a subtraction problem.

- Rewrite as an addition problem.

- The number line shows the difference.

- The difference between the elevations is 300 ft.

A balloon flies at 250 ft above sea level. A fish swims at 50 ft below sea level. What is the difference between these elevations?

$(+250) - (-50) = (+250) + (+50)$

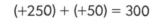

$(+250) + (+50) = 300$

> I remember! I can use additive inverses to subtract.

> **Number Lines** can be found on p.227.

A You can model addition on a number line.

DO Add $(-4) + (-3)$.

1. Start at 0 and draw an arrow for the first number.

2. Start at the end of the first arrow and draw an arrow for the second number.

3. Locate the end of the second arrow. Write the sum.

Draw the first arrow from _____ to _____.

Draw the second arrow from _____ to _____.

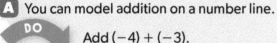

$(-4) + (-3) = $ _____.

B You can also model subtraction with a number line.

DO Subtract $(-2) - (-5)$.

1. Rewrite subtraction as addition of the opposite.

2. On a number line, draw the first arrow from 0 to -2. From -2, draw the second arrow, which is 5 units long.

3. Locate the end of the second arrow. Write the difference.

$(-2) - (-5) = $ _____ $+$ _____

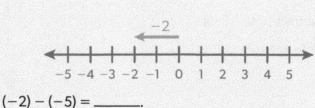

$(-2) - (-5) = $ _____.

DISCUSS To answer the subtraction problem $(-5) - (-8)$, Robert wrote the addition problem $5 + 8 = 13$. What would you tell Robert about his work?

PRACTICE

Use the number line to add or subtract.

1 Add (+3) + (−8).

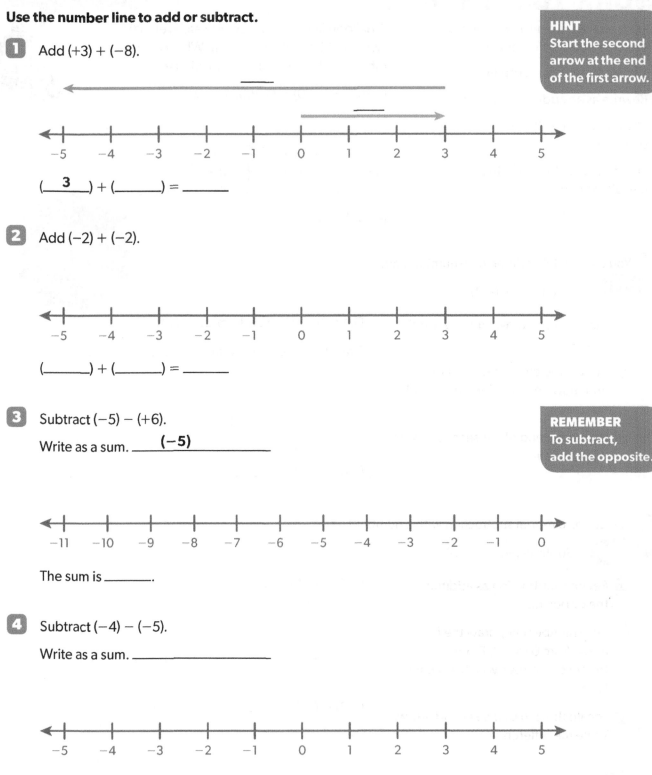

(___3___) + (_____) = _____

2 Add (−2) + (−2).

(_____) + (_____) = _____

3 Subtract (−5) − (+6).

Write as a sum. _____**(−5)**_____

The sum is _____.

4 Subtract (−4) − (−5).

Write as a sum. _____

The sum is _____.

Draw a number line to show subtraction.

5 Subtract $(-2) - (+4)$.

Write as a sum. _____

Number Lines can be found on p. 229.

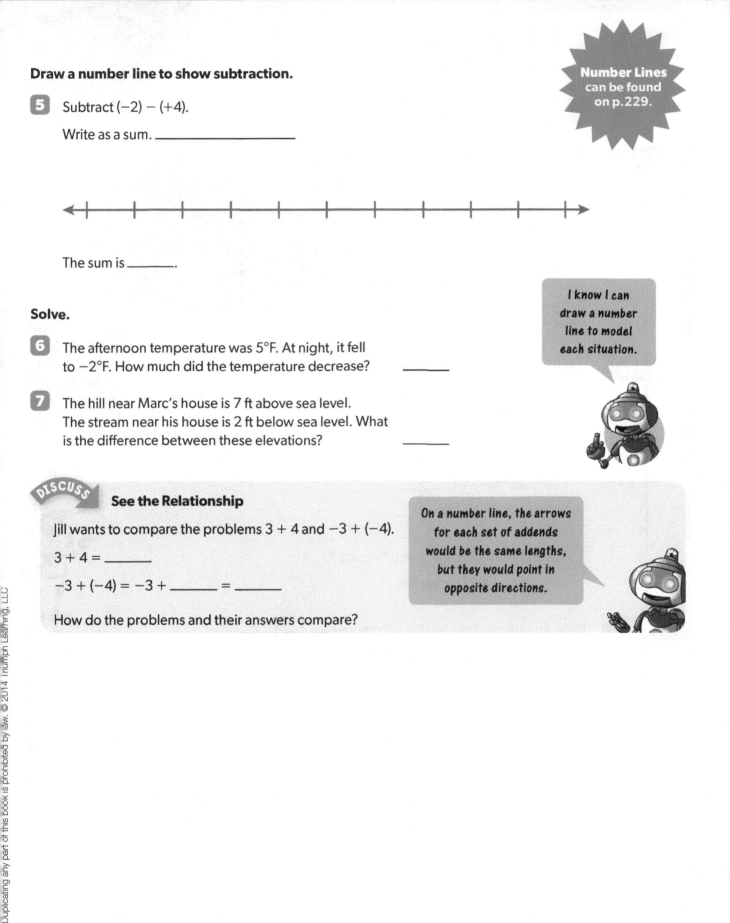

The sum is _____.

Solve.

6 The afternoon temperature was 5°F. At night, it fell to −2°F. How much did the temperature decrease? _____

7 The hill near Marc's house is 7 ft above sea level. The stream near his house is 2 ft below sea level. What is the difference between these elevations? _____

I know I can draw a number line to model each situation.

DISCUSS **See the Relationship**

Jill wants to compare the problems $3 + 4$ and $-3 + (-4)$.

$3 + 4 =$ _____

$-3 + (-4) = -3 +$ _____ $=$ _____

How do the problems and their answers compare?

On a number line, the arrows for each set of addends would be the same lengths, but they would point in opposite directions.

PROBLEM SOLVING

TIME FOR CHANGE

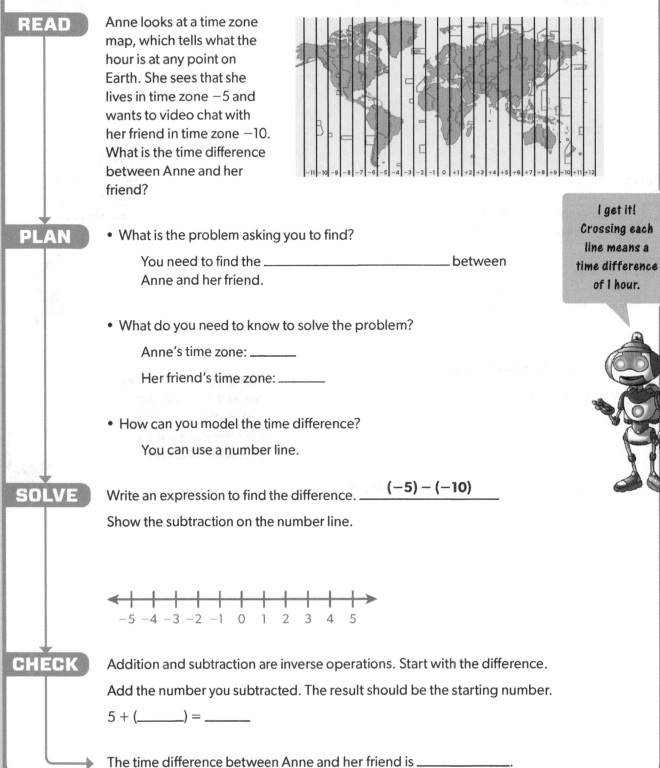

READ

Anne looks at a time zone map, which tells what the hour is at any point on Earth. She sees that she lives in time zone −5 and wants to video chat with her friend in time zone −10. What is the time difference between Anne and her friend?

I get it! Crossing each line means a time difference of 1 hour.

PLAN

• What is the problem asking you to find?

You need to find the _____ between Anne and her friend.

• What do you need to know to solve the problem?

Anne's time zone: _____

Her friend's time zone: _____

• How can you model the time difference?

You can use a number line.

SOLVE

Write an expression to find the difference. _____$(-5) - (-10)$_____

Show the subtraction on the number line.

CHECK

Addition and subtraction are inverse operations. Start with the difference.

Add the number you subtracted. The result should be the starting number.

$5 + ($ _____ $) =$ _____

The time difference between Anne and her friend is _____.

PRACTICE

Use the problem-solving steps to help you.

1 A company earned $7 million in one year. The next year, it lost $11 million. Did the company earn or lose money over the two years? How much was the gain or loss?

CHECKLIST
- [ ] READ
- [ ] PLAN
- [ ] SOLVE
- [ ] CHECK

2 Hank made a phone call from his home in Hong Kong (time zone +8) to New York City (time zone −5). What is the time difference between Hong Kong and New York City?

CHECKLIST
- [ ] READ
- [ ] PLAN
- [ ] SOLVE
- [ ] CHECK

3 The lowest point in California is Death Valley, at 282 ft below sea level. The highest point in Texas is Guadaloupe Mountain, at 8,749 ft above sea level. What is the difference in elevation between these two points?

CHECKLIST
- [ ] READ
- [ ] PLAN
- [ ] SOLVE
- [ ] CHECK

I remember!
I can use the additive inverse to solve, without using a number line.

LESSON 6 Multiplying Rational Numbers

PLUG IN Multiplying Fractions

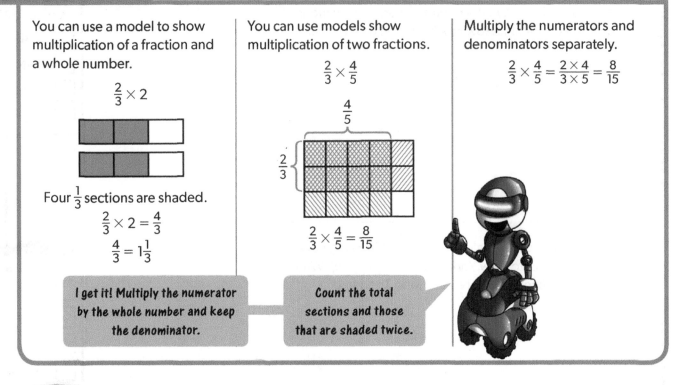

You can use a model to show multiplication of a fraction and a whole number.

$$\frac{2}{3} \times 2$$

Four $\frac{1}{3}$ sections are shaded.

$$\frac{2}{3} \times 2 = \frac{4}{3}$$

$$\frac{4}{3} = 1\frac{1}{3}$$

You can use models show multiplication of two fractions.

$$\frac{2}{3} \times \frac{4}{5}$$

$$\frac{2}{3} \times \frac{4}{5} = \frac{8}{15}$$

Multiply the numerators and denominators separately.

$$\frac{2}{3} \times \frac{4}{5} = \frac{2 \times 4}{3 \times 5} = \frac{8}{15}$$

I get it! Multiply the numerator by the whole number and keep the denominator.

Count the total sections and those that are shaded twice.

DISCUSS Tyrone says that the product of $\frac{3}{4}$ and 4 is 3. How could you check his answer without using a model?

A You can use models to help multiply a fraction by a whole number.

DO Find $\frac{3}{4} \times 3$.

1. Show 3 groups of $\frac{3}{4}$.
2. Find the number of shaded parts.
3. Write the product and simplify.

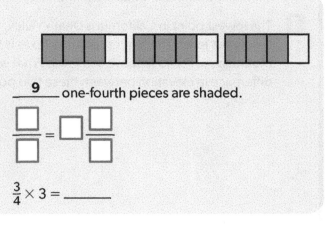

___9___ one-fourth pieces are shaded.

$$\frac{\square}{\square} = \square \frac{\square}{\square}$$

$$\frac{3}{4} \times 3 = \underline{\hspace{2cm}}$$

B You can multiply two fractions.

DO Find $\frac{4}{7} \times \frac{5}{6}$.

① Multiply the numerators and denominators separately.

② Simplify.

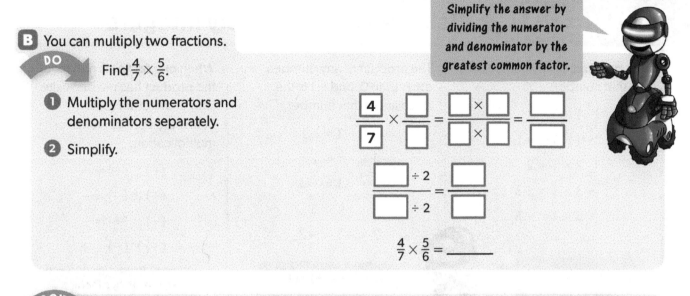

Simplify the answer by dividing the numerator and denominator by the greatest common factor.

$$\frac{4}{7} \times \frac{\square}{\square} = \frac{\square \times \square}{\square \times \square} = \frac{\square}{\square}$$

$$\frac{\square \div 2}{\square \div 2} = \frac{\square}{\square}$$

$$\frac{4}{7} \times \frac{5}{6} = \underline{\hspace{1cm}}$$

DISCUSS Peter says that the product of $\frac{1}{3} \times \frac{2}{6}$ will be equivalent to $\frac{1}{3}$, since $\frac{1}{3}$ and $\frac{2}{6}$ are equivalent fractions. Do you agree? Explain.

PRACTICE

Use the models to multiply. Simplify if necessary.

1 $\frac{1}{4} \times 5 = \dfrac{\square}{\square} = \square\dfrac{\square}{\square}$

2 $\frac{3}{5} \times 2 = \dfrac{\square}{\square} = \square\dfrac{\square}{\square}$

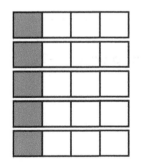

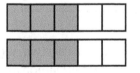

Find the product. Simplify if necessary.

3 $\frac{1}{3} \times \frac{4}{7}$

_____

4 $\frac{3}{4} \times \frac{2}{5}$

_____

5 $\frac{5}{6} \times 8$

_____

POWER UP — Using Rules to Multiply Integers

The **product** of any number and 1 is that number.

$$1 \times 1 = 1$$
$$-1 \times 1 = -1$$
$$2 \times 1 = 2$$
$$-3 \times 1 = -3$$
$$-5 \times 1 = -5$$

The product of any number, other than 0, and −1 is the opposite of that number.

$$1 \times -1 = -1$$
$$-1 \times -1 = 1$$
$$4 \times -1 = -4$$
$$-6 \times -1 = 6$$
$$7 \times -1 = -7$$

When one **factor** is negative, the product has the opposite sign of the other factor. Below are the sign rules for multiplication.

$$(+) \times (+) = +$$
$$(+) \times (-) = -$$
$$(-) \times (+) = -$$
$$(-) \times (-) = +$$

> So if I multiply a negative number by 1, the product is the same number, and the number is still negative.

> I see! When I multiply a number by −1, the product is the opposite of the number.

> I get it! If two factors have the same sign, their product is positive. If two factors have different signs, their product is negative.

Words to Know

product
the answer in a multiplication problem

$$-5 \quad \times \quad -2 \quad = \quad 10$$
↑
product

factor
a number that is multiplied to get a product

$$3 \quad \times \quad -2 \quad = \quad -6$$
↑ ↑
factor factor

DISCUSS Damon tries to multiply two negative numbers in his head. He says the product is −75. What would you tell Damon about his work?

A You can use sign rules to multiply integers.

DO Multiply −3 × −4.

❶ Determine whether the product is positive or negative.

❷ Multiply the factors without the signs.

❸ Write the product with the correct sign.

The signs of the two factors are the same, so the product is _____.

____**3**____ × _____ = _____

$$-3 \times -4 = \underline{\hspace{2cm}}$$

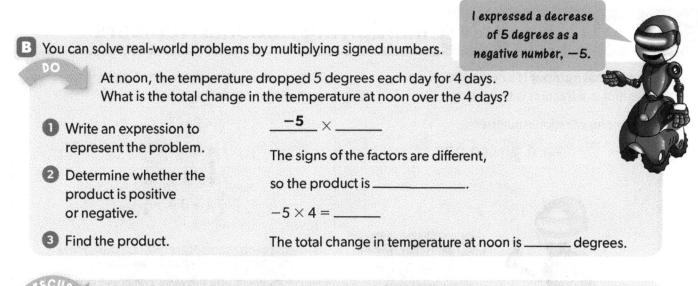

B You can solve real-world problems by multiplying signed numbers.

I expressed a decrease of 5 degrees as a negative number, −5.

DO

At noon, the temperature dropped 5 degrees each day for 4 days. What is the total change in the temperature at noon over the 4 days?

1 Write an expression to represent the problem.

___−5___ × _____

2 Determine whether the product is positive or negative.

The signs of the factors are different, so the product is _____.

−5 × 4 = _____

3 Find the product.

The total change in temperature at noon is _____ degrees.

DISCUSS

If the temperature at noon increased by 5 degrees for each of the four days, would you need to multiply the factors again to find the total change in temperature?

PRACTICE

Write whether the product is positive or negative.

1 4 × −12

_____

2 5 × −4 × −3

_____

Write each product.

3 −7 × 7 = _____

4 −7 × −7 = _____

5 1 × −6 = _____

6 −8 × 2 = _____

7 −2 × 6 × 2 = _____

8 −1 × −4 × −3 = _____

Solve. Include a positive or negative sign in the answer.

9 The price of a gallon of gas went down 3 cents each day for 4 days. Write a number that represents the change in price in cents.

_____

10 Ellen received two points of extra credit on each of her last five tests. Write a number to show her total number of points for extra credit.

_____

READY TO GO | Multiplying Rational Numbers

A **rational number** is a number than can be written as a fraction with integers.

Examples of rational numbers:

$$-4, 0, \frac{3}{8}, 1{,}000, 0.78$$

You can apply the rules for multiplying integers to multiplying rational numbers.

$$\frac{2}{5} \times 2 = \frac{4}{5}$$
$$-3 \times -4 = 12$$
$$-\frac{3}{4} \times \frac{1}{2} = -\frac{3}{8}$$
$$\frac{1}{4} \times -3 = -\frac{3}{4}$$

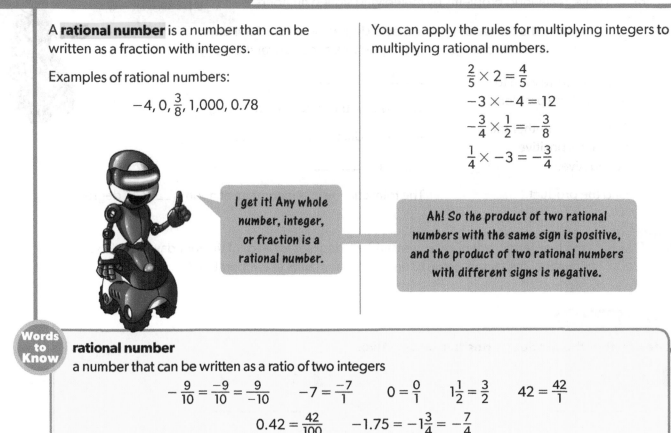

I get it! Any whole number, integer, or fraction is a rational number.

Ah! So the product of two rational numbers with the same sign is positive, and the product of two rational numbers with different signs is negative.

Words to Know

rational number

a number that can be written as a ratio of two integers

$$-\frac{9}{10} = \frac{-9}{10} = \frac{9}{-10} \qquad -7 = \frac{-7}{1} \qquad 0 = \frac{0}{1} \qquad 1\frac{1}{2} = \frac{3}{2} \qquad 42 = \frac{42}{1}$$

$$0.42 = \frac{42}{100} \qquad -1.75 = -1\frac{3}{4} = -\frac{7}{4}$$

DISCUSS When multiplying positive and negative fractions, Karen says she doesn't think about the signs of the factors until the last step. Explain if her method works.

LESSON LINK

PLUG IN

When multiplying two fractions, multiply the numerators and denominators separately.

$$\frac{2}{5} \times \frac{1}{3} = \frac{2 \times 1}{5 \times 3}$$
$$= \frac{2}{15}$$

POWER UP

Use the sign rules to help you multiply integers.

$$(-) \times (+) = -$$
$$-5 \times 6 = -30$$

GO!

I get it! Fractions and integers are rational numbers. I can apply the same rules to multiply all rational numbers.

WORK TOGETHER

You can use Number Cards and Number Cube to practice multiplying rational numbers.

- Choose two number cards. Use the numbers as the numerator and denominator of one fraction.

- Roll the number cube. If an even number is rolled, make your fraction positive. If an odd number is rolled, make your fraction negative.

- Repeat these steps to write another fraction.

- Find the product of these two fractions.

$-\dfrac{5}{6} \times \dfrac{2}{3}$

$= \dfrac{-5 \times 2}{6 \times 3}$

$= -\dfrac{10}{18}$

$= -\dfrac{5}{9}$

I see! I can generate rational numbers to multiply.

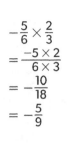

Number Cards and Number Cube can be found on pp. 237 and 241.

A Multiply a positive fraction by a negative integer.

DO Multiply $\dfrac{3}{7} \times -2$.

1. Determine whether the product is positive or negative.

2. Write each factor as a fraction.

3. Multiply the numerators and denominators separately.

4. Simplify if necessary.

The sign of the product will be _____.

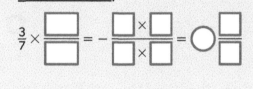

$\dfrac{3}{7} \times -2 = $ _____

B Multiply two negative rational numbers.

DO Find $-\dfrac{7}{9} \times -\dfrac{3}{5}$.

1. Determine whether the product is positive or negative.

2. Multiply the numerators and denominators separately.

3. Simplify if necessary.

The sign of the product will be _____.

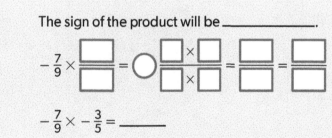

$-\dfrac{7}{9} \times -\dfrac{3}{5} = $ _____

DISCUSS How do the products of $\dfrac{1}{5} \times \dfrac{1}{6}$ and $-\dfrac{1}{5} \times -\dfrac{1}{6}$ compare. Why?

PRACTICE

Find the product. Simplify if necessary.

1 $\frac{3}{4} \times -4 =$ _____

> **REMEMBER**
> Write a whole number as a fraction with a denominator of 1.

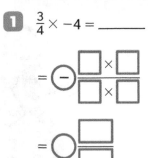

$= \ominus \dfrac{\square \times \square}{\square \times \square}$

$= \bigcirc \dfrac{\square}{\square}$

$=$ _____

2 $-\frac{4}{5} \times -\frac{7}{8} =$ _____

> **HINT**
> The product of two negative numbers is a positive number.

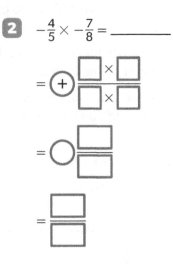

$= \oplus \dfrac{\square \times \square}{\square \times \square}$

$= \bigcirc \dfrac{\square}{\square}$

$= \dfrac{\square}{\square}$

3 $-\frac{7}{9} \times 6 =$ _____

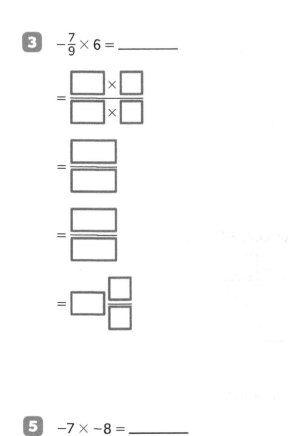

$= \dfrac{\square \times \square}{\square \times \square}$

$= \dfrac{\square}{\square}$

$= \dfrac{\square}{\square}$

$= \square \dfrac{\square}{\square}$

4 $-8 \times -\frac{2}{3} =$ _____

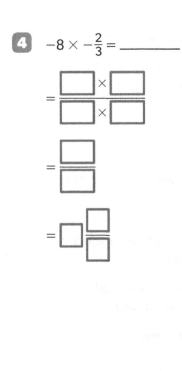

$= \dfrac{\square \times \square}{\square \times \square}$

$= \dfrac{\square}{\square}$

$= \square \dfrac{\square}{\square}$

5 $-7 \times -8 =$ _____

6 $-\frac{9}{10} \times -1 =$ _____

7 $-6 \times \frac{8}{9} =$ _____

8 $\frac{1}{2} \times -\frac{2}{3} =$ _____

Solve. Show your work.

9 Cereal boxes fill $\frac{3}{4}$ of each of 8 shelves at a grocery store. If the boxes are moved together, how many shelves will they fill?

The cereal boxes will fill _____ full shelves.

Solve.

10 Juanita read $\frac{2}{3}$ of a chapter of her math textbook every hour for five hours. How many chapters did she read all together?

_____

> I see! I have to decide whether the change is positive or negative.

11 The water level at a pond dropped $\frac{7}{10}$ of an inch per day for 15 days. What is the total change in the water level?

_____

> I get it! Finding part of a part is the same as multiplying a fraction by a fraction.

Multiply fractions to solve word problems.

Mrs. Williams cut $\frac{3}{4}$ of an apple pie into slices. $\frac{1}{2}$ of what she cut was eaten after dinner. What fraction of the pie was eaten?

How can the amount eaten be determined?

How much of the pie was eaten? _____

PROBLEM SOLVING

NOW WE'RE COOKING!

READ

Gabrielle's cookie recipe calls for $\frac{3}{4}$ cup of milk for one batch. If she wants to make $\frac{1}{2}$ batch of the cookies, how much milk should she use?

PLAN

- What is the problem asking you to find?

  how much _____

- What do you need to know to solve the problem?

  The recipe calls for _____ cup of milk in one batch.

  Gabrielle wants to make _____ batch of the cookies.

- How can you solve the problem?

  Find _____ of _____ cup of milk. So multiply $\dfrac{\square}{\square} \times \dfrac{\square}{\square}$.

SOLVE

Multiply the numerators and the denominators separately.

$$\dfrac{\boxed{1} \times \boxed{3}}{\square \times \square} = \dfrac{\square}{\square}$$

> I get it! The product is positive. That makes sense. You cannot have a negative amount of milk.

CHECK

If $\frac{3}{8}$ is $\frac{1}{2}$ of $\frac{3}{4}$, then 2 half batches should use $\frac{3}{4}$ cup of milk in all.

$$2 \times \dfrac{3}{8} = \dfrac{\square}{\square} = \dfrac{\square}{\square}$$

Gabrielle needs _____ cup of milk to make $\frac{1}{2}$ batch of cookies.

PRACTICE

Consider whether the answer should be negative or positive.

Use the problem-solving steps to help you.

1 In a board game, Oren had to move his piece backward 3 spaces for each of his last six turns. Find how far backward he moved during his last six turns.

CHECKLIST
- [ ] READ
- [ ] PLAN
- [ ] SOLVE
- [ ] CHECK

2 The audience at a movie theater filled $\frac{2}{3}$ of the seats in 20 rows. How many full rows could the audience fill in all?

CHECKLIST
- [ ] READ
- [ ] PLAN
- [ ] SOLVE
- [ ] CHECK

3 An airport had $\frac{1}{2}$ inch of rain every day for 6 days. There was $\frac{1}{4}$ inch of rain each day for the 6 following days. Find the total rain that was measured over all 12 days.

CHECKLIST
- [ ] READ
- [ ] PLAN
- [ ] SOLVE
- [ ] CHECK

Dividing Rational Numbers

PLUG IN Finding Quotients of Fractions

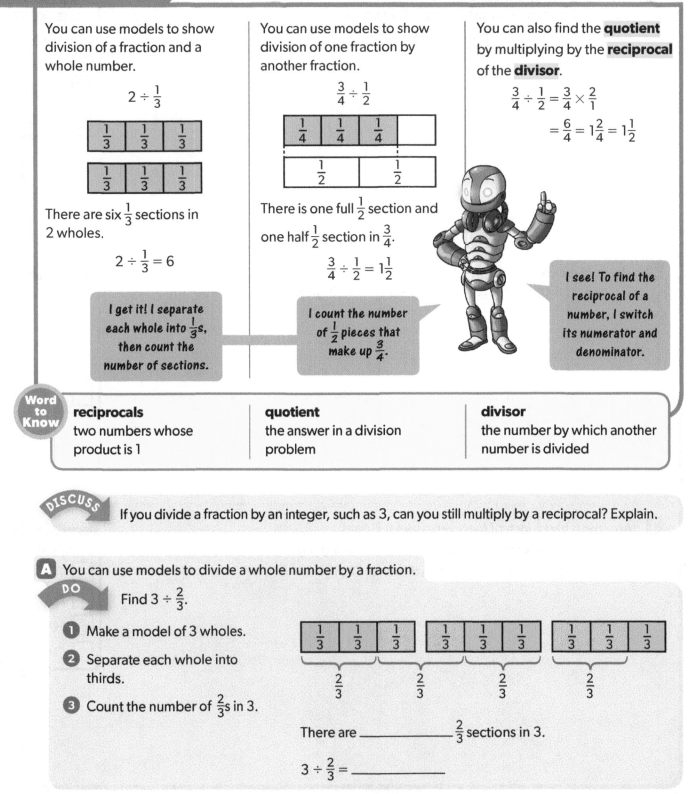

You can use models to show division of a fraction and a whole number.

$$2 \div \frac{1}{3}$$

| $\frac{1}{3}$ | $\frac{1}{3}$ | $\frac{1}{3}$ |

| $\frac{1}{3}$ | $\frac{1}{3}$ | $\frac{1}{3}$ |

There are six $\frac{1}{3}$ sections in 2 wholes.

$$2 \div \frac{1}{3} = 6$$

I get it! I separate each whole into $\frac{1}{3}$s, then count the number of sections.

You can use models to show division of one fraction by another fraction.

$$\frac{3}{4} \div \frac{1}{2}$$

| $\frac{1}{4}$ | $\frac{1}{4}$ | $\frac{1}{4}$ | |

| $\frac{1}{2}$ | $\frac{1}{2}$ |

There is one full $\frac{1}{2}$ section and one half $\frac{1}{2}$ section in $\frac{3}{4}$.

$$\frac{3}{4} \div \frac{1}{2} = 1\frac{1}{2}$$

I count the number of $\frac{1}{2}$ pieces that make up $\frac{3}{4}$.

You can also find the **quotient** by multiplying by the **reciprocal** of the **divisor**.

$$\frac{3}{4} \div \frac{1}{2} = \frac{3}{4} \times \frac{2}{1}$$
$$= \frac{6}{4} = 1\frac{2}{4} = 1\frac{1}{2}$$

I see! To find the reciprocal of a number, I switch its numerator and denominator.

Word to Know

reciprocals
two numbers whose product is 1

quotient
the answer in a division problem

divisor
the number by which another number is divided

DISCUSS If you divide a fraction by an integer, such as 3, can you still multiply by a reciprocal? Explain.

A You can use models to divide a whole number by a fraction.

DO Find $3 \div \frac{2}{3}$.

① Make a model of 3 wholes.

② Separate each whole into thirds.

③ Count the number of $\frac{2}{3}$s in 3.

| $\frac{1}{3}$ | $\frac{1}{3}$ | $\frac{1}{3}$ | $\frac{1}{3}$ | $\frac{1}{3}$ | $\frac{1}{3}$ | $\frac{1}{3}$ | $\frac{1}{3}$ | $\frac{1}{3}$ |

$\frac{2}{3}$ $\frac{2}{3}$ $\frac{2}{3}$ $\frac{2}{3}$

There are _____ $\frac{2}{3}$ sections in 3.

$$3 \div \frac{2}{3} = \underline{\hspace{2cm}}$$

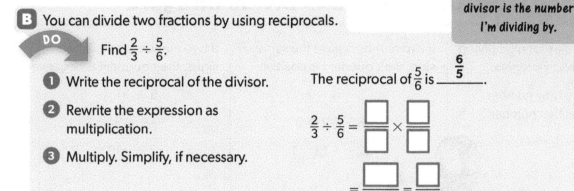

B You can divide two fractions by using reciprocals.

DO Find $\frac{2}{3} \div \frac{5}{6}$.

1 Write the reciprocal of the divisor.

2 Rewrite the expression as multiplication.

3 Multiply. Simplify, if necessary.

The reciprocal of $\frac{5}{6}$ is $\dfrac{6}{5}$.

$$\frac{2}{3} \div \frac{5}{6} = \frac{\square}{\square} \times \frac{\square}{\square}$$

$$= \frac{\square}{\square} = \frac{\square}{\square}$$

I remember! The divisor is the number I'm dividing by.

DISCUSS Deval says $\frac{3}{4} \div \frac{1}{2}$ is the same as $\frac{1}{2} \div \frac{3}{4}$. What would you tell Deval about his work?

PRACTICE

Use the model to divide.

1 $\frac{7}{10} \div \frac{1}{5}$

$\frac{1}{10}$	$\frac{1}{10}$	$\frac{1}{10}$	$\frac{1}{10}$	$\frac{1}{10}$	$\frac{1}{10}$	$\frac{1}{10}$	$\frac{1}{10}$	$\frac{1}{10}$	$\frac{1}{10}$

$\frac{1}{5}$	$\frac{1}{5}$	$\frac{1}{5}$	$\frac{1}{5}$	$\frac{1}{5}$

Fraction Strips can be found on p.213.

There are _____ $\frac{1}{5}$ sections in $\frac{7}{10}$.

Find the quotient. Simplify if necessary.

2 $\frac{7}{8} \div \frac{1}{6} = \dfrac{\boxed{7}}{\boxed{8}} \times \dfrac{\square}{\square}$

$= \dfrac{\square}{\square}$

$= \square\dfrac{\square}{\square}$

$= \square\dfrac{\square}{\square}$

3 $\frac{6}{7} \div 3 = \dfrac{\square}{\square} \times \dfrac{\square}{\square}$

$= \dfrac{\square}{\square}$

$= \dfrac{\square}{\square}$

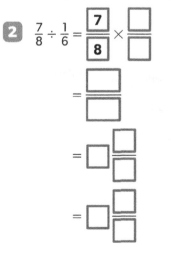
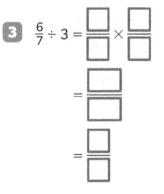

Using Rules to Divide Integers

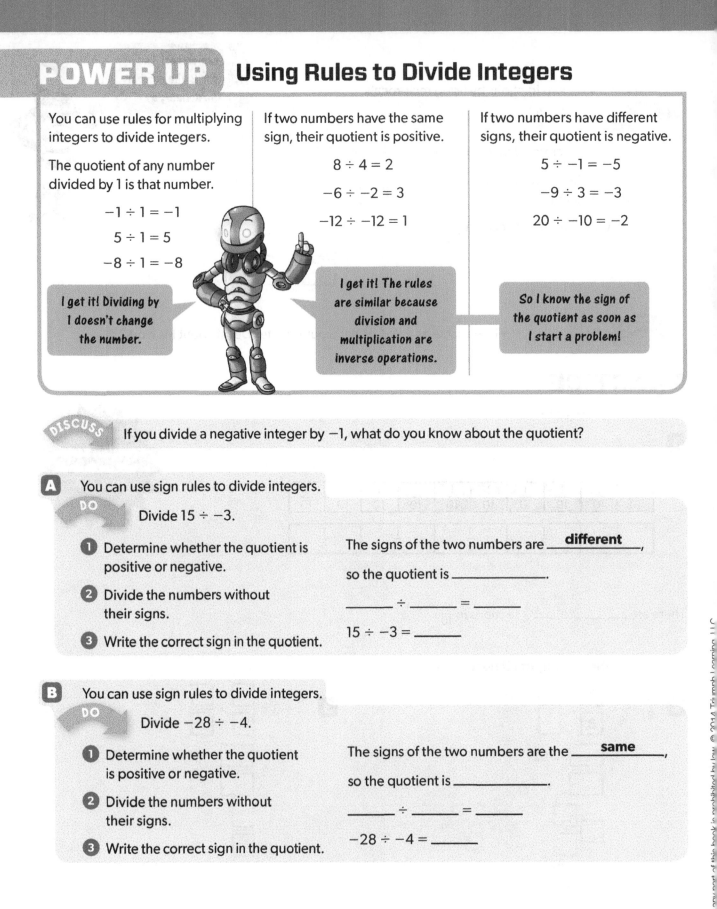

You can use rules for multiplying integers to divide integers.

The quotient of any number divided by 1 is that number.

$$-1 \div 1 = -1$$
$$5 \div 1 = 5$$
$$-8 \div 1 = -8$$

If two numbers have the same sign, their quotient is positive.

$$8 \div 4 = 2$$
$$-6 \div -2 = 3$$
$$-12 \div -12 = 1$$

If two numbers have different signs, their quotient is negative.

$$5 \div -1 = -5$$
$$-9 \div 3 = -3$$
$$20 \div -10 = -2$$

I get it! Dividing by 1 doesn't change the number.

I get it! The rules are similar because division and multiplication are inverse operations.

So I know the sign of the quotient as soon as I start a problem!

DISCUSS If you divide a negative integer by −1, what do you know about the quotient?

A You can use sign rules to divide integers.

DO Divide $15 \div -3$.

1. Determine whether the quotient is positive or negative.

2. Divide the numbers without their signs.

3. Write the correct sign in the quotient.

The signs of the two numbers are ___**different**___,

so the quotient is _____.

_____ $\div$ _____ = _____

$15 \div -3 =$ _____

B You can use sign rules to divide integers.

DO Divide $-28 \div -4$.

1. Determine whether the quotient is positive or negative.

2. Divide the numbers without their signs.

3. Write the correct sign in the quotient.

The signs of the two numbers are the ___**same**___,

so the quotient is _____.

_____ $\div$ _____ = _____

$-28 \div -4 =$ _____

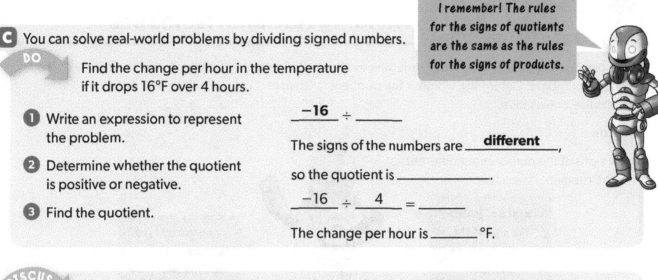

C You can solve real-world problems by dividing signed numbers.

I remember! The rules for the signs of quotients are the same as the rules for the signs of products.

Find the change per hour in the temperature if it drops 16°F over 4 hours.

❶ Write an expression to represent the problem.

❷ Determine whether the quotient is positive or negative.

❸ Find the quotient.

_____ −16 _____ ÷ _____

The signs of the numbers are ___**different**___,

so the quotient is _____.

_____ −16 _____ ÷ _____ 4 _____ = _____

The change per hour is _____ °F.

DISCUSS

The price of gas increased the same amount each week for 6 weeks. During that time, the price increased a total of 24 cents. Peter said the price change was −4 cents per week. Explain how you know Peter is incorrect without dividing.

PRACTICE

Write whether the quotient is positive or negative.

1 $8 \div -8$

_____

2 $-21 \div -3$

_____

Find the quotient.

3 $-9 \div 1 =$ _____

4 $16 \div -1 =$ _____

5 $21 \div -3 =$ _____

6 $-43 \div -43 =$ _____

Solve. Include a positive or negative sign in the answer.

7 The temperature increased the same amount every day for 5 days. During that time, the temperature increased 15 degrees in all. Write the number that represents the change per day, in degrees.

_____

8 Tony took out $200 from his bank account over 5 weeks. He took out the same amount each week. Write a number that shows the weekly change, in dollars, in his account.

_____

Dividing Rational Numbers

You can apply the rules for dividing integers to all rational numbers. Determine whether the quotient is positive or negative.

Divide $-\frac{2}{5} \div \frac{2}{7}$.

The signs of the numbers are different, so the quotient is negative.

> I see! So I'll know the sign of the quotient before I divide.

Divide by multiplying by the reciprocal of the divisor.

$$-\frac{2}{5} \div \frac{2}{7} = -\frac{2}{5} \times \frac{7}{2}$$
$$= \frac{-14}{10}$$
$$= \frac{-7}{5}$$
$$= -1\frac{2}{5}$$

> I remember! I flip the numerator and the denominator to find the reciprocal.

DISCUSS Tom says that to divide 4 by $-\frac{1}{3}$, he uses the rules to determine that the sign of the quotient is negative, and then he multiplies 4×3. Do you agree? Explain.

LESSON LINK

PLUG IN

You can rewrite division by a fraction as multiplication by its reciprocal.

$$\frac{1}{8} \div \frac{3}{4}$$
$$= \frac{1}{8} \times \frac{4}{3}$$
$$= \frac{4}{24}$$
$$= \frac{1}{6}$$

POWER UP

You can divide with integers by following the rules for signs.

$$(+) \div (+) = (+)$$
$$8 \div 4 = 2$$
$$(-) \div (-) = (+)$$
$$-15 \div -3 = 5$$
$$(+) \div (-) = (-)$$
$$11 \div -11 = -1$$
$$(-) \div (+) = (-)$$
$$-12 \div 3 = -4$$

GO!

> I get it! I can extend the rules for division with integers to division with all rational numbers.

WORK TOGETHER

Use Number Cards and Number Cube to practice dividing rational numbers.

- Choose two number cards. Use the numbers as the numerator and denominator of one fraction.

- Roll the number cube. If an even number is rolled, make your fraction positive. If the number rolled is odd, make your fraction negative.

- Repeat these steps to write another fraction.

- Find the quotient of these two fractions.

Use Number Cards and Number Cube to make rational numbers.

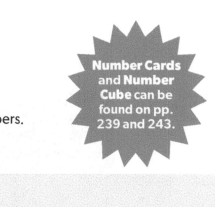

$$\frac{2}{3} \div -\frac{1}{3}$$
$$= \frac{2}{3} \times -\frac{3}{1}$$
$$= -\frac{6}{3}$$
$$= -2$$

I can generate rational numbers to divide!

Number Cards and **Number Cube** can be found on pp. 239 and 243.

A Divide a positive fraction by a negative integer.

DO Divide $\frac{2}{5} \div -3$.

1. Determine whether the quotient is positive or negative.

2. Rewrite as multiplication by the reciprocal of the divisor.

3. Multiply the numerators and the denominators separately.

4. Simplify if necessary.

The sign of the quotient will be _____.

$$\frac{2}{5} \times \frac{\square}{\square} = \frac{\square \times \square}{\square \times \square} = \bigcirc\frac{\square}{\square}$$

$$\frac{2}{5} \div -3 = \text{_____}$$

B Divide two negative rational numbers.

DO Divide $-\frac{1}{2} \div -\frac{1}{3}$.

1. Determine whether the quotient is positive or negative.

2. Rewrite as multiplication by the reciprocal of the divisor.

3. Multiply the numerators and the denominators separately.

4. Simplify if necessary.

The sign of the quotient will be _____.

$$-\frac{1}{2} \times \frac{\square}{\square} = \frac{\square \times \square}{\square \times \square} = \bigcirc\frac{\square}{\square} = \square\frac{\square}{\square}$$

$$-\frac{1}{2} \div -\frac{1}{3} = \text{_____}.$$

DISCUSS Without dividing, explain how the quotients of $\frac{3}{4} \div \frac{1}{5}$ and $\frac{3}{4} \div -\frac{1}{5}$ compare.

PRACTICE

Find the quotient. Simplify if necessary.

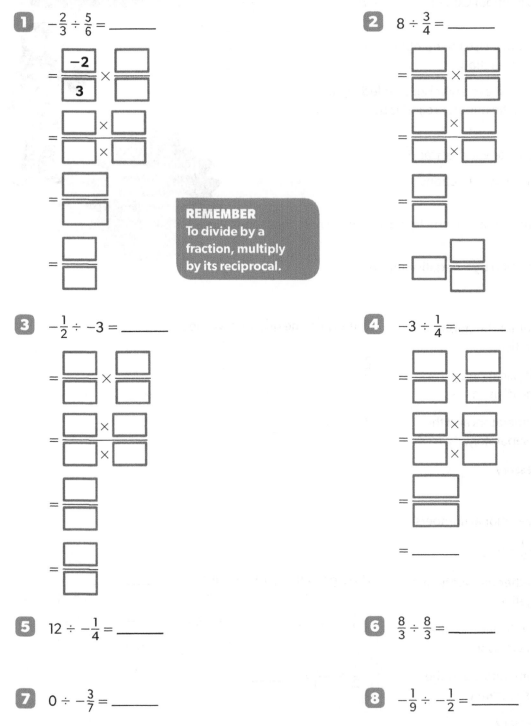

1 $-\frac{2}{3} \div \frac{5}{6} =$ _____

2 $8 \div \frac{3}{4} =$ _____

REMEMBER
To divide by a fraction, multiply by its reciprocal.

3 $-\frac{1}{2} \div -3 =$ _____

4 $-3 \div \frac{1}{4} =$ _____

5 $12 \div -\frac{1}{4} =$ _____

6 $\frac{8}{3} \div \frac{8}{3} =$ _____

7 $0 \div -\frac{3}{7} =$ _____

8 $-\frac{1}{9} \div -\frac{1}{2} =$ _____

Divide. Write the quotient as a mixed number. Show your work.

9 $-50 \div 6 =$ _____

10 $-7 \div -\frac{3}{5} =$ _____

Write an equation to solve.

11 Darla uses 20 square feet of fabric to make eight pillowcases of the same size. How many square feet of fabric are in each pillowcase?

_____

12 The resale value of a car decreases by $50 every week. After how many weeks will the value of the car decrease by $500?

_____

I know! I can write division by a whole number as multiplication by its reciprocal.

DISCUSS **Decide How to Use Division.**

Four friends went to dinner. Their bill was $41, including tax. They agreed to leave a $7 tip. If they divide the total cost equally, how much should each pay?

How can they determine the cost per person?

What is the total cost divided by the number of people?

The total cost includes the bill and the tip.

PROBLEM SOLVING

BUILDING A QUOTIENT

READ

A construction company has $504 to pay four workers for seven hours of work each. How many dollars will be paid to each worker per hour?

PLAN

• What is the problem asking you to find?

the _____ for each worker

• What do you need to know to solve the problem?

There is _____ available. The number of workers is _____.

The number of hours for each is _____.

• How can you solve the problem?

Divide _____ by 4 workers.

Divide that quotient by 7 hours.

SOLVE

Write an equation.

Let h = amount per hour.

(__504__ ÷ _____) ÷ _____ = h

Divide one step at a time.

_____ ÷ _____ = _____

The amount per hour is $_____.

CHECK

Work backward.

Multiply the quotient by the hours for each worker. _____ × _____

Multiply that product by the number of workers. _____ × _____

The product should be the total amount of money. _____

Each worker will receive $_____ per hour.

> Multiplication and division are inverse operations.

PRACTICE

Use the problem-solving steps to help you.

1 Malik ran a total of 3 miles around his high school track. Each lap around the track is $\frac{1}{4}$ mile. How many laps did Malik run?

CHECKLIST
- [ ] READ
- [ ] PLAN
- [ ] SOLVE
- [ ] CHECK

2 The water level in a leaky swimming pool fell by the same amount each day for 6 days. Over that time, the water level measured 4 inches lower. What was the change in the water level each day?

I remember! I'll think about whether a change should be shown as a positive or negative number.

CHECKLIST
- [ ] READ
- [ ] PLAN
- [ ] SOLVE
- [ ] CHECK

3 Molly's thermometer outside her house showed that the temperature fell 8 degrees in the last 12 hours. What was the change in the temperature per hour during that time?

CHECKLIST
- [ ] READ
- [ ] PLAN
- [ ] SOLVE
- [ ] CHECK

4 Salman baked 2 pounds of brownies to serve to friends. If each brownie weighed $\frac{1}{16}$ of a pound, how many brownies did he bake?

CHECKLIST
- [ ] READ
- [ ] PLAN
- [ ] SOLVE
- [ ] CHECK

Problem Solving with Rational Numbers

PLUG IN Problem Solving with Whole Numbers

Abby bought a shirt for $18 and shoes for $35. She had $80 before she went shopping. How much does she have now?

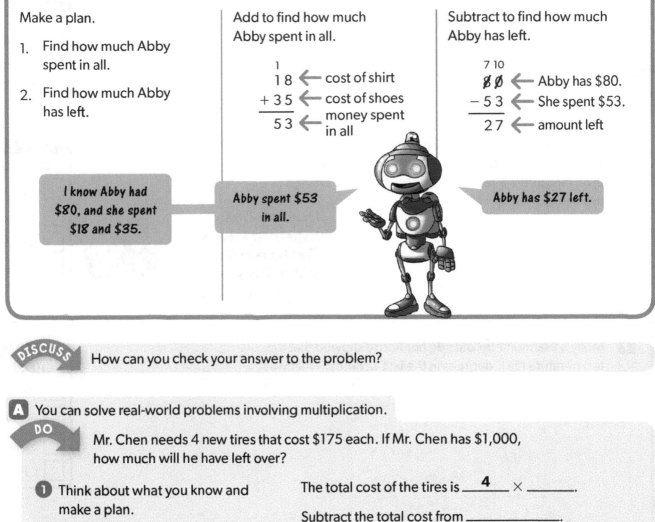

Make a plan.

1. Find how much Abby spent in all.

2. Find how much Abby has left.

Add to find how much Abby spent in all.

$$\begin{array}{r} \overset{1}{}1\,8 \leftarrow \text{cost of shirt} \\ +\ 3\,5 \leftarrow \text{cost of shoes} \\ \hline 5\,3 \leftarrow \text{money spent in all} \end{array}$$

Subtract to find how much Abby has left.

$$\begin{array}{r} \overset{7\ 10}{\cancel{8}\,\cancel{0}} \leftarrow \text{Abby has \$80.} \\ -\ 5\,3 \leftarrow \text{She spent \$53.} \\ \hline 2\,7 \leftarrow \text{amount left} \end{array}$$

I know Abby had $80, and she spent $18 and $35.

Abby spent $53 in all.

Abby has $27 left.

DISCUSS How can you check your answer to the problem?

A You can solve real-world problems involving multiplication.

DO

Mr. Chen needs 4 new tires that cost $175 each. If Mr. Chen has $1,000, how much will he have left over?

① Think about what you know and make a plan.

② Multiply to find the total cost of the tires.

③ Subtract to find how much Mr. Chen has left.

The total cost of the tires is ___**4**___ × _____.

Subtract the total cost from _____.

$$\begin{array}{r} 1\,7\,5 \\ \times\ \ \ \ 4 \\ \hline \end{array}$$

The cost of 4 tires is $_____.

1,000 − _____ = _____

Mr. Chen will have $_____ left over.

B You can solve real-world problems involving division.

DO

An auditorium has 256 seats. There are 8 equal rows. How many seats are in each row?

> The quotient tells me how many are in each group.

❶ Think about what you know and make a plan.

❷ Divide to find the number of seats in each row.

❸ Write the quotient.

The number of seats in each row is

_____ 256 _____ ÷ _____.

8⟌256

There are _____ seats in each row.

DISCUSS

Will solving word problems always require the same number of steps?

PRACTICE

Solve.

1 During a meteor shower, Sophia counted 76 meteors in the first hour. In the second hour, she counted 114 meteors. How many meteors did she count in all?

_____ meteors

2 A scientist finds a white tiger that weighs about 400 pounds. She sees a striped tiger that weighs about 220 pounds. How much more does the white tiger weigh than the striped tiger?

_____ pounds

3 A tree farm has 45 rows of trees with 36 trees in each row. How many trees are there in all?

_____ trees

4 A book contains 225 pages. Jenelle plans to read 15 pages per day. How long will it take her to finish the book?

_____ days

5 Every night, Zach reads for 45 minutes and practices piano for 30 minutes. How long does he spend reading and playing piano over 4 nights?

_____ minutes

6 Eggs are shipped in large boxes that contain 20 egg cartons. Each egg carton holds 12 eggs. How many eggs are in 5 large boxes?

_____ eggs

Simplifying Complex Fractions

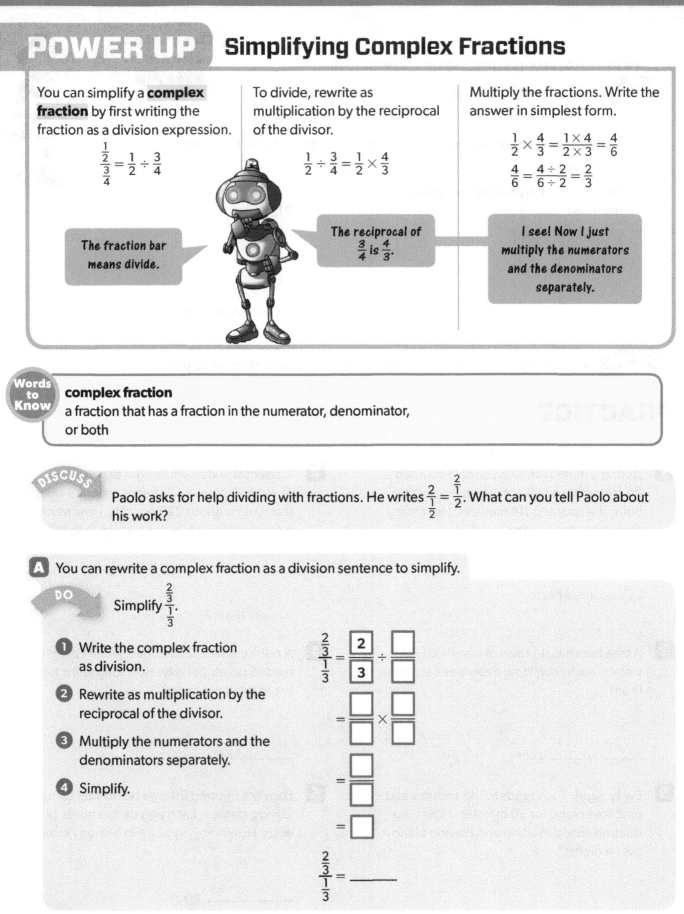

You can simplify a **complex fraction** by first writing the fraction as a division expression.

$$\frac{\frac{1}{2}}{\frac{3}{4}} = \frac{1}{2} \div \frac{3}{4}$$

The fraction bar means divide.

To divide, rewrite as multiplication by the reciprocal of the divisor.

$$\frac{1}{2} \div \frac{3}{4} = \frac{1}{2} \times \frac{4}{3}$$

The reciprocal of $\frac{3}{4}$ is $\frac{4}{3}$.

Multiply the fractions. Write the answer in simplest form.

$$\frac{1}{2} \times \frac{4}{3} = \frac{1 \times 4}{2 \times 3} = \frac{4}{6}$$

$$\frac{4}{6} = \frac{4 \div 2}{6 \div 2} = \frac{2}{3}$$

I see! Now I just multiply the numerators and the denominators separately.

Words to Know

complex fraction
a fraction that has a fraction in the numerator, denominator, or both

DISCUSS

Paolo asks for help dividing with fractions. He writes $\frac{2}{\frac{1}{2}} = \frac{\frac{2}{1}}{2}$. What can you tell Paolo about his work?

A You can rewrite a complex fraction as a division sentence to simplify.

DO

Simplify $\frac{\frac{2}{3}}{\frac{1}{3}}$.

① Write the complex fraction as division.

② Rewrite as multiplication by the reciprocal of the divisor.

③ Multiply the numerators and the denominators separately.

④ Simplify.

$$\frac{\frac{2}{3}}{\frac{1}{3}} = \frac{\boxed{2}}{\boxed{3}} \div \frac{\square}{\square}$$

$$= \frac{\square}{\square} \times \frac{\square}{\square}$$

$$= \frac{\square}{\square}$$

$$= \square$$

$$\frac{\frac{2}{3}}{\frac{1}{3}} = \underline{\hspace{2cm}}$$

B You can divide fractions by whole numbers.

DO Simplify $\frac{\frac{1}{3}}{6}$.

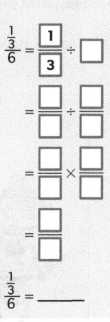

1 Write the fraction as division.

$\frac{\frac{1}{3}}{6} = \frac{\boxed{1}}{\boxed{3}} \div \boxed{}$

2 Write the whole number as a fraction with a denominator of 1.

$= \frac{\boxed{}}{\boxed{}} \div \frac{\boxed{}}{\boxed{}}$

3 Rewrite as multiplication by the reciprocal of the divisor.

$= \frac{\boxed{}}{\boxed{}} \times \frac{\boxed{}}{\boxed{}}$

4 Multiply the numerators and the denominators separately.

$= \frac{\boxed{}}{\boxed{}}$

$\frac{\frac{1}{3}}{6} = \underline{\hspace{2cm}}$

DISCUSS Lee says he could simplify $\frac{\frac{3}{4}}{3}$ or $\frac{3}{\frac{4}{3}}$ and he'd get the same answer. Is Lee correct? Show your work.

PRACTICE

Simplify the complex fraction.

1 $\dfrac{\frac{1}{2}}{\frac{1}{6}} = \dfrac{\boxed{1}}{\boxed{2}} \div \dfrac{\boxed{1}}{\boxed{6}} = \underline{\hspace{1.5cm}}$

2 $\dfrac{\frac{1}{4}}{\frac{3}{8}} = \underline{\hspace{1.5cm}}$

3 $\dfrac{\frac{3}{10}}{\frac{2}{5}} = \underline{\hspace{1.5cm}}$

4 $\dfrac{\frac{3}{4}}{\frac{3}{8}} = \underline{\hspace{1.5cm}}$

5 $\dfrac{12}{\frac{2}{3}} = \underline{\hspace{1.5cm}}$

6 $\dfrac{\frac{4}{5}}{4} = \underline{\hspace{1.5cm}}$

You can solve real-world problems with rational numbers just as you solved problems with whole numbers.

Lisa lives $1\frac{2}{3}$ miles from school. Dan lives $2\frac{4}{5}$ miles from school. How much farther from the school does Dan live than Lisa?

1 **Write What You Need to Find**
the difference between how far Dan lives from school and how far Lisa lives from school

2 **Write What You Know**
Lisa lives $1\frac{2}{3}$ miles from school.

Dan lives $2\frac{4}{5}$ miles from school.

3 **Make a Plan and Compute.**
Write a subtraction expression. Rewrite the mixed numbers with common denominators. Subtract.

Dan lives $1\frac{2}{15}$ miles farther from school than Lisa.

$$2\frac{4}{5} - 1\frac{2}{3}$$

$$2\frac{4}{5} \rightarrow 2\frac{12}{15}$$

$$1\frac{2}{3} \rightarrow -1\frac{10}{15}$$

$$\overline{\qquad 1\frac{2}{15}}$$

> 15 is the least common denominator of 3 and 5.

DISCUSS Dominic learned about complex fractions, but he wonders if he'd be able to divide rational numbers to solve real-word problems. Explain a method he could use.

LESSON LINK

PLUG IN

You can solve problems with whole numbers by writing what you know, then deciding what you are trying to find.

Darren divides 36 pencils among 4 friends. How many pencils does each friend get?

$$36 \div 4 = 9 \text{ pencils}$$

POWER UP

You can simplify complex fractions by writing as division, then rewriting as multiplication by the reciprocal of the divisor.

$$\frac{\frac{1}{8}}{\frac{1}{6}} = \frac{1}{8} \div \frac{1}{6}$$

$$= \frac{1}{8} \times \frac{6}{1}$$

$$= \frac{6}{8}$$

$$= \frac{3}{4}$$

GO!

> I get it! I can use the same methods for solving problems with whole numbers to solve problems with rational numbers.

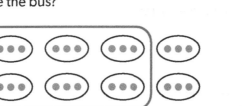

I see! I have to find the number that is $\frac{6}{8}$ of 24.

WORK TOGETHER

You can use Counters to solve problems involving multiplication with rational numbers.

- Each counter represents 1 student.

- The denominator of $\frac{6}{8}$ tells how many equal groups.

- The numerator of $\frac{6}{8}$ tells you to count the number in 6 of these groups.

- 18 students ride the bus.

There are 24 students in Ms. William's class. If $\frac{6}{8}$ of the class rides a bus to school, how many students ride the bus?

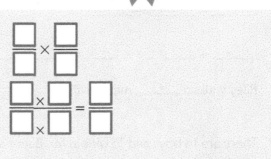

$\frac{6}{8}$ of 24 is 18.

$\frac{6}{8} \times 24 = \frac{6 \times 24}{8} = \frac{144}{8} = 18$

Counters can be found on p. 223.

A You can multiply rational numbers to solve problems.

DO

A punch recipe calls for $\frac{3}{4}$ gallon of ice cream. Jasmine wants to cut the recipe in half. How much ice cream does she need?

1 Write an expression to represent the problem.

2 Multiply the numerators and denominators.

3 Write the product.

Jasmine needs _____ gallon of ice cream.

B You can divide rational numbers to solve problems.

DO

Mason has a piece of wood that is $4\frac{1}{2}$ meters long. He cuts the wood into 5 equal pieces. How long is each smaller piece?

1 Write an expression to represent the problem.

2 Write the mixed number as an improper fraction.

3 Multiply by the reciprocal of the divisor.

4 Write the quotient.

Each piece of wood is _____ meter long.

DISCUSS

Henry is trying to find the product of $\frac{3}{5}$ and 15. He divided 15 counters into 3 groups. He says that there are 5 counters in each group, so the answer is 5. What can you tell Henry about his work?

PRACTICE

Write an expression to represent the problem then solve.

1 A baker is considering buying a $\frac{3}{4}$-pound bag of flour or a $\frac{5}{8}$-pound bag of flour. How much heavier is the larger bag?

$\frac{3}{4}$ _____ − _____

_____ − _____ = _____

The larger bag weighs _____ pound more.

REMEMBER
Find a common denominator to add or subtract fractions.

2 Riley walked $5\frac{3}{4}$ miles on Tuesday, $\frac{7}{12}$ mile on Wednesday, and $4\frac{2}{3}$ miles on Thursday. How many miles did she walk in all?

_____ + _____ + _____

_____ + _____ + _____ = _____

Riley walked _____ miles in all.

3 There are 14 boys and 15 girls in Mr. Bauer's class. If each student brings in 5 cans of food for a food drive, how many cans will the class collect?

$\frac{14}{}$ + $\frac{15}{}$ = _____

_____ × _____ = _____

The class will collect _____ cans in all.

HINT
First, find the total number of students in the class.

4 A chef used $\frac{4}{5}$ pound of cheese and $\frac{1}{10}$ pound of peppers on a pizza. How much more of a pound of cheese than of peppers did the chef use?

_____ − _____

_____ − _____ = _____

The chef used _____ pound more cheese.

Solve.

5 Carl has $\frac{3}{4}$ gallon of milk. How many cups of milk does he have if one cup is equal to $\frac{1}{16}$ of a gallon?

_____

I remember! I can use division to find part of a fraction.

6 In Ms. Duncan's class, $\frac{3}{4}$ of the students have pets. Of that group, $\frac{2}{3}$ have dogs. What fraction of the class has dogs?

_____

DISCUSS **Reason**

Dante says he can check solutions for division problems by multiplying the quotient by the divisor, even when he divides fractions. Use Dante's reasoning to solve and check the problems below.

I remember! The number I am dividing by is the divisor; the number I'm dividing into is the dividend.

Divide $\frac{5}{12} \div \frac{2}{3}$.

$$\frac{5}{12} \div \frac{2}{3} = \frac{5}{12} \times \frac{3}{2}$$

$$= \frac{\boxed{}}{\boxed{}}$$

$$= \frac{\boxed{}}{\boxed{}}$$

Check your answer.

$$\frac{\boxed{}}{\boxed{}} \times \frac{2}{3} = \frac{\boxed{}}{\boxed{}}$$

$$= \frac{\boxed{}}{\boxed{}}$$

Divide $\frac{3}{5} \div \frac{1}{10}$.

$$\frac{3}{5} \div \frac{1}{10} = \frac{3}{5} \times \frac{10}{1}$$

$$= \frac{\boxed{}}{\boxed{}}$$

$$= \frac{\boxed{}}{\boxed{}}$$

Check your answer.

$$\frac{\boxed{}}{\boxed{}} \times \frac{1}{10} = \frac{\boxed{}}{\boxed{}}$$

$$= \frac{\boxed{}}{\boxed{}}$$

Explain why you agree or disagree with Dante.

PROBLEM SOLVING

DOG WALKING

READ

Jack walks his dog $\frac{3}{4}$ mile every day. It takes him $\frac{1}{3}$ hour to walk that distance. How fast does he walk in miles per hour?

PLAN

• What is the problem asking you to find?

You need to find how fast Jack walks in _____**miles**_____ per _____.

• What do you need to know to solve the problem?

Jack walks _____ mile.

It takes him _____ hour.

• How can you solve the problem?

The answer is in miles per hour. Divide the distance, in miles, by the time, in hours.

SOLVE

Write a division expression to represent the problem.

$\dfrac{\text{distance}}{\text{time}} \nearrow \dfrac{\frac{3}{4}\ \text{mile}}{\frac{1}{3}\ \text{hour}}$

$\dfrac{\Box}{\Box} \div \dfrac{\Box}{\Box} = \dfrac{\Box}{\Box} \times \dfrac{\Box}{\Box} = \dfrac{\Box}{\Box}$

Write the answer as a mixed number. _____

CHECK

Use the inverse operation.

$\Box\dfrac{\Box}{\Box} \times \dfrac{1}{3} = \dfrac{\Box}{\Box} \times \dfrac{1}{3} = \dfrac{\Box}{\Box} = \dfrac{\Box}{\Box}$

> Multiply the quotient by the divisior, $\frac{1}{3}$.

Jack walks _____ miles per hour.

I remember! I look for key words to decide which operation to use.

PRACTICE

Use the problem-solving steps to help you.

1 Emma starts at one end of a $4\frac{1}{2}$-mile-long bike trail. After riding $2\frac{3}{10}$ miles, she stops for water. How much farther does she need to ride to reach the end of the trail?

CHECKLIST

☐ READ

☐ PLAN

☐ SOLVE

☐ CHECK

2 Ethan's dog weighs 48 pounds. Noah's dog weighs $\frac{5}{8}$ the weight of Ethan's dog. How much does Noah's dog weigh?

CHECKLIST

☐ READ

☐ PLAN

☐ SOLVE

☐ CHECK

3 Mia has $\frac{3}{4}$ pound of butter. A muffin recipe calls for $\frac{1}{8}$ pound of butter for each batch. How many batches of muffins can Mia make with the butter she has?

CHECKLIST

☐ READ

☐ PLAN

☐ SOLVE

☐ CHECK

Factoring and Expanding Linear Expressions

PLUG IN
Recognizing and Generating Equivalent Expressions

You can write **equivalent expressions** by combining **like terms**.

To rename $3x + 5x - 2x$, add and subtract the coefficients to combine like terms.

$$3x + 5x - 2x = (3 + 5 - 2)x = 6x$$

You can also write equivalent expressions by using the **Distributive Property**.

To rename $3(2y + 4)$, multiply each addend by 3 and simplify.

$$3(2y + 4) = (3 \times 2y) + (3 \times 4)$$
$$= 6y + 12$$

I see! A coefficient is a number that multiplies a variable. 3 is the coefficient for 3x.

I got it! 6y and 12 do not have the same variable, They are not like terms, so I cannot combine them.

Words to Know

equivalent expressions
expressions that are equal in value and can be transformed into each other by using operations

$$5x + 7x = 12x$$

like terms
terms in which the variables are the same, although the coefficients may be different

$$6x, -5x, 3\tfrac{1}{2}x, 2.5x$$

distributive property
a mathematical rule that states the following:

$$a \times (b + c) = ab + ac$$
$$a \times (b - c) = ab - ac$$
$$5(2x + y) = 10x + 5y$$
$$3(6 - b) = 18 - 3b$$

DISCUSS You know you can add whole numbers. Are they like terms? Explain.

A You can write equivalent expressions by combining like terms.

DO Write an expression equivalent to $2a + 8a + 2b + 4b$.

❶ Group like terms. (___2a___ + ___8a___) + (_____ + _____)

❷ Add the coefficients of like terms. (_____ + _____)_____ + (_____ + _____)_____

❸ Write the simplified expression. _____ + _____

B You can use the distributive property to write equivalent expressions.

> I see! The factors are positive, and addition is used, so the products are positive.

DO Write an expression equivalent to $2(5x + 7)$.

① Multiply 2 by each addend.

$2(5x + 7) = \underline{\quad 2 \quad} \times \underline{\quad 5x \quad} + \underline{\qquad} \times \underline{\qquad}$

② Find the product of each term.

$\underline{\qquad} + \underline{\qquad}$

③ Check that each term has the correct sign.

C You can determine if expressions are equivalent by using the distributive property.

DO Is $4(x+2) + 3x + 7$ equivalent to $7x + 14$?

① Distribute.

$\underline{\quad 4x \quad} + \underline{\quad 8 \quad} + \underline{\qquad} + \underline{\qquad}$

② Group like terms.

$(\underline{\qquad} + \underline{\qquad}) + (\underline{\qquad} + \underline{\qquad})$

③ Combine like terms.

$\underline{\qquad} + \underline{\qquad}$

④ Compare.

Are the expressions equivalent? $\underline{\qquad}$

DISCUSS Lana uses the distributive property to write $3(3x - 5)$ as $3x - 15$? What can you tell Lana about her work?

PRACTICE

Distribute to write an equivalent expression.

1 $2(a - 4b) = \underline{\qquad}$

2 $-3(8 - 2x) = \underline{\qquad}$

3 $\left(\frac{1}{4}\right)(20 + 4x) = \underline{\qquad}$

4 $-\frac{1}{9}(27a - 81b) = \underline{\qquad}$

Combine like terms to write an equivalent expression.

5 $2a + 5b - 4a + 2b = \underline{\qquad}$

6 $\frac{3}{2}x + 5 + \frac{5}{2}x + 7 = \underline{\qquad}$

Determine if the following pairs of expressions are equivalent.

7 $4y - 20$ and $-4(5 - y) = \underline{\qquad}$

8 $-2x - 14$ and $-2(x - 7) = \underline{\qquad}$

Using the Distributive Property to Factor an Expression

Factor $5d + 10$ completely.

To find the **greatest common factor (GCF)**, list the terms and their factors.

There are two terms: $5d$ and 10.

Since $5d$ is equal to $5 \times d$, its factors are 1, 5, and d.

The factors of 10 are 1, 2, 5, and 10.

The GCF is 5.

> To list factors, I write every number and variable that divides a term evenly.

Use the distributive property to factor 5 from each term of the expression.

$$5d + 10 = (5 \times d) + (5 \times 2)$$
$$= 5(d + 2)$$

The factored form of $5d + 10$ is $5(d + 2)$.

> I see! In factored form, I can see which factor is common to each term of $5d + 10$.

Words to Know

greatest common factor (GCF)
the largest integer and/or common variable that divides evenly into all of 2 or more terms

DISCUSS

Robert says $4n + 5n$ cannot be factored because 4 and 5 do not have a common factor. Is he correct? Explain.

A You can find the greatest common factor (GCF) of two or more terms.

DO

What is the GCF of $6y$, $30y$, and 15?

1. List the factors of each term.

2. Find the GCF of the terms.

Factors of $6y$: ___1___, ___2___, _____, _____, _____

Factors of $30y$: _____, _____, _____, _____,

_____, _____, _____, _____, _____

Factors of 15: _____, _____, _____, _____

The GCF of $6y$, $30y$, and 15 is _____.

I remember! The first step of factoring is finding the GCF of the terms.

B You can factor an expression with one variable.

DO

Factor $24s + 32$.

1. List the factors of each term.
2. Find the GCF of the terms.
3. Use the distributive property to factor the expression.

Factors of $24s$: ___1___, ___2___, _____,

_____, _____, _____, _____, _____, _____

Factors of 32: _____, _____, _____, _____,

_____, _____

The greatest common factor is _____.

$24s + 32 = ($ _____ $\times$ _____ $) + ($ _____ $\times$ _____ $)$

$24s + 32 =$ _____ $($ _____ $+$ _____ $)$

DISCUSS

To factor $12s - 6$ completely, Amir writes $3(4s - 2)$. What can you tell him about his work?

PRACTICE

Find the GCF of the terms.

1 $81b$ and 18

Factors of $81b$: _____, _____, _____,

_____, _____, _____

Factors of 18: _____, _____, _____,

_____, _____, _____

The GCF is _____.

2 $42j$ and 12

Factors of $42j$: _____, _____, _____,

_____, _____, _____, _____, _____,

_____

Factors of 12: _____, _____, _____,

_____, _____, _____

The GCF is _____.

Factor each expression completely.

3 $3c - 9 =$ _____ $($ _____ $-$ _____ $)$

4 $56w + 7 =$ _____ $($ _____ $+$ _____ $)$

5 $15f - 10 =$ _____ $($ _____ $-$ _____ $)$

6 $16k + 34 =$ _____ $($ _____ $+$ _____ $)$

7 $12i + 36 =$ _____ $($ _____ $+$ _____ $)$

8 $44h - 22 =$ _____ $($ _____ $-$ _____ $)$

Factoring and Expanding Linear Expressions

You can use the distributive property to expand linear expressions with rational numbers.

$$\frac{1}{12}(y + 6) = \left(\frac{1}{12} \times y\right) + \left(\frac{1}{12} \times 6\right)$$

$$= \frac{y}{12} + \frac{6}{12} = \frac{y}{12} + \frac{1}{2}$$

$$2.5(2z - 1) = (2.5 \times 2z) - (2.5 \times 1)$$

$$= 5z - 2.5$$

> I see! Expanding is multiplying, so it is the opposite process of factoring.

You can factor expressions whose terms have one or more common factors.

$$100a + 48ab$$

Factors of 100a: 1, 2, 4, 5, 10, 20, 25, 50, 100, a

Factors of 48ab: 1, 2, 3, 4, 6, 8, 12, 16, 24, 48, a, b

The common factors are 1, 2, 4, and a.

The GCF is 4a.

$$100a + 48ab = (4a \times 25) + (4a \times 12b)$$

$$= 4a(25 + 12b)$$

> I get it! I can factor any expression if I can find the GCF of the terms.

DISCUSS Can you use the distributive property to expand, factor, or both? Explain.

LESSON LINK

PLUG IN	POWER UP	GO!

You can combine like terms to write equivalent expressions.

$$m + 2m = (1 + 2)m$$

$$= 3m$$

$$4(n + 1) = (4 \times n) + (4 \times 1)$$

$$= 4n + 4$$

You can find the greatest common factor to factor an expression.

$$40p + 10$$

Factors of 40p: 1, 2, 4, 5, 8, 10, 20, 40, p

Factors of 10: 1, 2, 5, 10

The GCF is 10.

$$40p + 10 = (10 \times 4p) + (10 \times 1)$$

$$= 10(4p + 1)$$

> I see! I can use the distributive property to expand and factor linear expressions.

I use parentheses to group each set of factors.

WORK TOGETHER

You can use the distributive property to expand expressions with rational numbers.

- Multiply each term inside the parentheses by the outside factor.

- Simplify.

- $4(7.5t - 0.3) = 30t - 1.2$

Expand $4(7.5t - 0.3)$.

$$4(7.5t - 0.3) = (4 \times 7.5t) - (4 \times 0.3)$$
$$= 30t - 1.2$$

A You can expand a linear expression that includes fractions.

DO Expand $\frac{3}{8}\left(\frac{4}{5}u + \frac{8}{9}\right)$.

1 Multiply each term inside the parentheses by the outside factor.

2 Simplify.

3 Simplify the fractions if necessary.

$$\frac{3}{8}\left(\frac{4}{5}u + \frac{8}{9}\right) = \left(\frac{\square}{\square} \times \frac{\square}{\square}u\right) + \left(\frac{\square}{\square} \times \frac{\square}{\square}\right)$$

$$= \frac{\square}{\square}u + \frac{\square}{\square} = \frac{\square}{\square}u + \frac{\square}{\square}$$

B You can factor an expression with two variables.

DO Factor $24g + 56h$ completely.

1 Find the GCF of the terms.

2 Rewrite the terms with the GCF as one of the factors.

3 Use the distributive property to factor the expression.

Factors of $24g$: _____, _____, _____, _____,

_____, _____, _____, _____, _____

Factors of $56h$: _____, _____, _____, _____,

_____, _____, _____, _____, _____

The greatest common factor is _____.

$24g + 56h = ($_____ $\times$ _____$) + ($_____ $\times$ _____$)$

$24g + 56h =$ _____ $($_____ $+$ _____$)$

Seema factors the expression $30r + 36s$ as $6r(5 + 6s)$. What can you tell her about her work?

PRACTICE

Factor the expression completely.

1 $75x - 15y$

_____**15**_____ (____**5x**____ − _____)

> **HINT**
> Look for the greatest common factors.

2 $56x - 7xy$

3 $35xy - 7x + 49x$

4 $6u + 12uy + 18u$

____**6u**____ (_____ + _____ + _____)

_____ (_____ + _____)

> **REMEMBER**
> Combine like terms after factoring to simplify the expression.

Expand the expression.

5 $0.1(40t + 1)$

_____ + _____

6 $-\frac{1}{2}\left(\frac{3}{4}m + 8\right)$

7 $3\left(2x - \frac{2}{3}y\right)$

8 $0.5y\,(7 - 2 + 0.7)$

Write an equivalent expression.

9 The perimeter of this rectangle is represented by the expression $2\left(\frac{1}{3} + y\right)$. Expand to write an equivalent expression.   _____

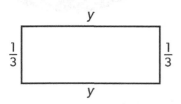

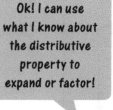

Ok! I can use what I know about the distributive property to expand or factor!

10 The surface area of a box of height 1, length 2, and width w is equal to the expression $4 + 2w + 4w$. Factor and simplify to write an equivalent expression.   _____

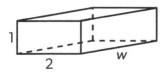

DISCUSS

Think Through the Process

Keith needs to factor the following expression:

$0.2xyz - 4xz$

I know! The GCF can include variables, too!

He knows that the first step is to find the greatest common factor for both terms.

Explain the steps Keith needs to take to factor the expression.

PROBLEM SOLVING

Science Club

JOIN THE CLUB!

READ Joan has pins made for the science club. The pins cost $0.65 each, and she pays an additional fee of $90 with each order. Write an expression to show the total cost if Joan places 4 separate orders and buys *n* pins each time.

PLAN • What is the problem asking you to find?

an expression that shows how much Joan pays for ___4___ pin orders

• What do you need to know to write the expression?

The cost of each pin is _____. The additional fee is _____.

Joan places _____ separate orders. Each order has _____ pins.

SOLVE Write the expression that models this situation.

The cost of the pins in each order is _____.

The total cost per order is _____ + _____.

The total cost for all orders is ___4___ × (_____ + _____).

Use the distributive property to expand the expression.

___4___ (_____ + _____) = _____ + _____.

CHECK Pick a number of pins in each order. Then compare the cost by using the information in the problem and using your expression.

Assume that Joan buys 100 pins in each order.

Find the cost of pins per order. $0.65 × _____ + $90 = _____

Find the cost for four orders. 4 × _____ = _____

Now use the expression and *n* = 100.

$2.60 × _____ + $360 = _____

The expression _____ shows the total cost.

I can use the distributive property to multiply any rational number, including $\frac{1}{2}$, by each addend in a sum!

PRACTICE

Use the problem-solving steps to help you.

1 Alana buys one shirt with a regular price of *p* dollars and 2 sweaters with a regular price of *s* dollars. She uses a coupon so that she pays only half the regular price. Write an expression that shows how much money Alana spends in all. Then expand the expression.

CHECKLIST
- [ ] READ
- [ ] PLAN
- [ ] SOLVE
- [ ] CHECK

2 Molly buys dinner for her family. She buys *x* burgers at $1.80 each and *y* milkshakes at $1.50 each. She also pays $0.10 of tax for every dollar she spends. Write an expression that shows how much tax she pays. Then expand the expression.

CHECKLIST
- [ ] READ
- [ ] PLAN
- [ ] SOLVE
- [ ] CHECK

3 For his birthday party, Enrique rents 7 tables at *t* dollars each and 56 chairs at *c* dollars each. Write an expression that shows his total cost, and factor it completely.

CHECKLIST
- [ ] READ
- [ ] PLAN
- [ ] SOLVE
- [ ] CHECK

Applying Properties to Solve Problems

PLUG IN Estimation Strategies

You can **estimate** the solution to a problem by using values that are easier to work with. You can estimate by **rounding**.

Estimate the sum of 23.7 + 34.5.

23.7 rounds to 24.

34.5 rounds to 35.

24 + 35 = 59

23.7 + 34.5 is about 59.

> I see! We rounded each number to the nearest one.

You can also estimate a solution by using **compatible numbers**.

Estimate the quotient of 632 ÷ 8.

Use 640 and 8, since they are compatible numbers, and 640 is close to 632.

640 ÷ 8 = 80

632 ÷ 8 is about 80.

> This makes sense! Sometimes it's faster to work with numbers that are easy to divide.

Words to Know

estimate	**rounding**	**compatible numbers**
to find a number that is close to an exact answer	approximating a number to its nearest place value	numbers that are easy to compute mentally

DISCUSS Is either method for estimating — rounding or using compatible numbers — better than the other to get the exact answer? Explain.

A You can use rounding to estimate differences.

DO Last week, Anna ran $13\frac{1}{3}$ miles and Bruce ran 9.75 miles. Estimate how many more miles Anna ran than Bruce last week.

1 Round each number to the nearest whole number.

2 Subtract the estimated values.

3 Find the estimated difference.

$13\frac{1}{3}$ miles is about ___**13**___ miles.

9.75 miles is about _____ miles.

_____ − _____ = _____ miles

Anna ran about _____ more miles than Bruce last week.

B You can also use compatible numbers to estimate quotients.

To choose compatible numbers to divide, think of two numbers, one of which is a multiple of the other.

DO

There are 14 weeks in one semester of school. Each student needs to complete 120 math topics each semester. About how many math topics does a student need to complete each week?

1 Write an expression to represent the problem.

$\underline{\quad 120 \quad} \div \underline{\quad 14 \quad}$

2 Identify compatible numbers.

120 and _____ are compatible numbers, and _____ is close to 14.

3 Use compatible numbers to divide.

_____ ÷ _____ = _____

4 Find the estimated quotient.

A student needs to complete about _____ math topics each week.

DISCUSS

Francis is ordering his birthday cake. He thinks there will be about 20 people at his party. He also thinks that each person will eat a $\frac{1}{2}$-pound slice of cake. How does this situation show when estimation is useful?

PRACTICE

Use rounding to estimate.

1 123 − 89 is about ___30___.

2 17.95 + 23.22 is about _____.

3 $3\frac{7}{8} \times 2\frac{1}{9}$ is about _____.

4 $23\frac{4}{5} + 33.12$ is about _____.

Use compatible numbers to estimate.

5 32 × 9 is about _____.

6 189 ÷ 3 is about _____.

7 37 × 5 is about _____.

8 289 ÷ 7 is about _____.

Solve.

9 Brittany downloaded an album that cost $9.89, bought a poster that cost $3.89, and ordered a T-shirt that cost $12.48. Estimate the total cost of all three items.

_____

10 A pack of 5 pairs of socks costs $11.99. About how much does each pair of socks cost?

_____

POWER UP

Using Properties of Operations to Solve Problems

You can use the **Commutative Property** to add or multiply numbers.

$$18 + 23 = 23 + 18$$

$$41 = 41$$

$$6 \times 4 = 4 \times 6$$

$$24 = 24$$

Changing the order of the addends or factors does not change the sum or product.

You can also use the **Associative Property** to add or multiply numbers.

$$(3 + 4) + 5 = 3 + (4 + 5)$$

$$7 + 5 = 3 + 9$$

$$12 = 12$$

$$(3 \times 4) \times 5 = 3 \times (4 \times 5)$$

$$12 \times 5 = 3 \times 20$$

$$60 = 60$$

I see! Changing the grouping of the addends or factors does not change the sum or product.

The **Identity Property** is also useful for solving problems.

$$5 + 0 = 5$$

$$5 \times 1 = 5$$

I get it! If I add 0 to any number or multiply it by 1, the result is that number.

Words to Know

commutative property
a property of addition and multiplication that states that the order of the addends or factors does not affect the sum or product

associative property
a property of addition and multiplication that states that the grouping of addends or factors does not affect the sum or product

identity property
a property of addition and multiplication that states that the sum of a number and zero is that number, and the product of a number and one is that number

DISCUSS The commutative property always works for addition and multiplication. Does it always work with subtraction or division? Give an example.

A You can use the commutative property to solve problems.

DO Three packages weigh 5.2 pounds, 3.7 pounds, and 4.8 pounds. What is the total weight of all three packages

❶ Write an expression to represent the problem.

❷ Rewrite the expression by using the commutative property.

__5.2__ + __3.7__ + __4.8__

__5.2__ + _____ + _____

_____ + _____ = _____

I see! I can move the two numbers that are easier to add next to each other.

The total weight of the packages is _____ pounds.

❸ Add.

❹ Write the sum.

I get it! Converting a fraction to an equivalent decimal makes it easier to compute.

B You can use the associative property to solve problems.

DO

Add $\left(8 + 3\frac{1}{4}\right) + 2.75$.

1 Convert the fraction to a decimal.

$(\underline{\quad 8 \quad} + \underline{\quad\quad}) + \underline{\quad 2.75 \quad}$

2 Rewrite the expression by using the associative property.

$\underline{\quad 8 \quad} + (\underline{\quad\quad} + \underline{\quad\quad})$

$\underline{\quad\quad} + (\underline{\quad\quad}) = \underline{\quad\quad}$

3 Add.

$\left(8 + 3\frac{1}{4}\right) + 2.75 = \underline{\quad\quad}$

4 Write the sum.

DISCUSS

Carter rewrites the expression $(3 + 14) + 17$ as $14 + (3 + 17)$. Carter says that he applied the commutative property and then the associative property. Are the expressions equivalent? Explain.

PRACTICE

First, use the property to rewrite the expression. Then, find the sum or product.

1 Associative Property

$\left(3\frac{1}{2} + 1.32\right) + 3.28$

$\underline{\quad 3\frac{1}{2} + (1.32 + 3.28) \quad}$

_____

2 Commutative Property

1.5×88.8

_____

_____

3 Commutative Property

$20.2 + 45\frac{3}{5} + 33.8$

_____

_____

4 Associative Property

$2 \times (5 \times 19.1)$

_____

_____

Solve.

5 Reagan walked 3.2 miles on Saturday, $4\frac{1}{2}$ miles on Sunday, and 2.8 miles on Monday. How many miles did she walk in all?

_____ miles

6 This week, Isaac has spent 1.5 hours on science homework, $2\frac{1}{4}$ hours on math homework, and 3 hours reading. How long did Isaac spend on science, math, and reading this week?

_____ hours

READY TO GO

Applying Properties to Solve Problems

You can use properties of operations to solve problems and use estimation to check your work.

Patrick bought $2\frac{1}{4}$ pounds of ham, 3.8 pounds of turkey, and 2.75 pounds of cheese. How many pounds of food did he buy in all?

1 Write an expression to represent the problem.

$2\frac{1}{4} + 3.8 + 2.75$

2 Convert $2\frac{1}{4}$ to a decimal.

$2\frac{1}{4} + 3.8 + 2.75 = 2.25 + 3.8 + 2.75$

3 Rewrite the expression by using the commutative property. Add.

$2.25 + 2.75 + 3.8$

$5 + 3.8 = 8.8$

4 Use estimation to check your answer.

$2\frac{1}{4}$ or 2.25 is about 2, 2.75 is about 3, and 3.8 is about 4.

$2 + 3 + 4 = 9$

9 is close to 8.8. The answer makes sense.

Patrick bought 8.8 pounds of food.

> I can use estimation to check the reasonableness of my answer.

DISCUSS Patrick used rounding to estimate. What numbers could he have used if he wanted to estimate with compatible numbers?

LESSON LINK

PLUG IN	**POWER UP**	**GO!**
Rounding and compatible numbers are useful estimation strategies.	**Properties of operations can help you solve problems.**	I get it! I can use properties to solve problems and use estimation to check my answer.
Estimate $775 + 123$.	Commutative Property	
1 Use rounding. $780 + 120 = 900$	$4 + 5 = 5 + 4$	
	$4 \times 5 = 5 \times 4$	
2 Use compatible numbers. $775 + 125 = 900$	Associative Property	
	$8 + (2 + 9) = (8 + 2) + 9$	
	$5 \times (4 \times 4.8) = (5 \times 4) \times 4.8$	

WORK TOGETHER

You can apply properties to solve real-world problems. Use estimation to check your answer.

- The expression represents the problem.

- The expression is rewritten by using the commutative property.

- Add to get a sum of $5\frac{1}{3}$.

- To check, each mixed number is rounded to the nearest whole number and added.

- The estimated sum, 5, is close to the actual sum, $5\frac{1}{3}$. The answer is reasonable.

- The banner is $5\frac{1}{3}$ feet long.

Darcy taped 3 poster boards together to make a long banner. The lengths of the posters are $2\frac{3}{4}$ feet, $1\frac{1}{3}$ feet, and $1\frac{1}{4}$ feet. How long is the banner?

$$2\frac{3}{4} + 1\frac{1}{3} + 1\frac{1}{4}$$

$$2\frac{3}{4} + 1\frac{1}{4} + 1\frac{1}{3}$$

$$4 + 1\frac{1}{3} = 5\frac{1}{3}$$

Check:

$$2\frac{3}{4} + 1\frac{1}{4} + 1\frac{1}{3}$$
$$\downarrow \qquad \downarrow \qquad \downarrow$$
$$3 + 1 + 1 = 5 \leftarrow \text{close to } 5\frac{1}{3}$$

> I can look at the fraction part of the mixed numbers and reorder the addends to make it easier to add.

A Solve by using the associative property.

DO

This weekend, James spent 2.25 hours on history homework, 1.75 hours on math homework, and 3.5 hours studying for a math test. How many hours did James spend on history and math this weekend?

1. Write an expression to represent the problem.

2. Use the associative property to regroup the addends.

3. Add.

4. To check, round each decimal to the nearset whole number.

5. Add to find the estimated sum and compare to the actual sum.

6. Write the answer.

$2.25 + (1.75 + 3.5)$

$(\underline{\qquad} + \underline{\qquad}) + 3.5$

$(\underline{\qquad}) + \underline{\qquad} = \underline{\qquad}$

2.25 rounds to $\underline{\qquad}$.

1.75 rounds to $\underline{\qquad}$.

3.5 rounds to $\underline{\qquad}$.

$\underline{\qquad} + \underline{\qquad} + \underline{\qquad} = \underline{\qquad}$

$\underline{\qquad}$ is close to $\underline{\qquad}$, so the answer is reasonable.

James spent $\underline{\qquad}$ hours on history and math homework.

DISCUSS

To compute $(4 \times 7) + 10$, Kyle writes the following:

By the associative property, $(4 \times 7) + 10 = 4 \times (7 + 10)$.

By the commutative property, $4 \times (7 + 10) = 4 \times (10 + 7)$.

How would you help Kyle to better understand using properties?

> Pay attention to the operations in the expression.

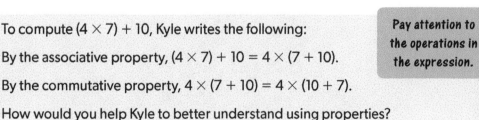

PRACTICE

Solve. Use estimation to check your answer.

1 Shelby ran 2.25 miles on Sunday, 2.5 miles on Monday, and $3\frac{3}{4}$ miles on Tuesday. How many miles did Shelby run in all?

HINT
Look for pairs of addends that are easier to add.

$\underline{\quad 2.25 \quad} + \underline{\qquad} + \underline{\qquad}$

2 Micia spent 19 minutes driving to the grocery store, 30 minutes at the grocery store, 10 minutes driving to the library, 21 minutes at the library, and 15 minutes driving home. How many minutes passed from the time Micia left home to the time she returned?

$\underline{\qquad} + \underline{\qquad} + \underline{\qquad} + \underline{\qquad} + \underline{\qquad} = \underline{\qquad}$

3 Lee is mixing fuel for his lawn mower. It takes $5\frac{1}{2}$ cups of gasoline, $\frac{1}{10}$ cup of oil, and $\frac{1}{2}$ cup of fuel additive. How much fuel will Lee mix in all?

$\Box\dfrac{\Box}{\Box} + \dfrac{\Box}{\Box} + \dfrac{\Box}{\Box}$

4 Margot's recipe for one batch of cinnamon rolls calls for $\frac{3}{4}$ cup of sugar. She plans to make $\frac{1}{5}$ batch of cinnamon rolls, and she will give $\frac{1}{3}$ of this to her neighbor. How much sugar will be in her neighbor's cinnamon rolls?

$\dfrac{\Box}{\Box} \times \left(\dfrac{\Box}{\Box} \times \dfrac{\Box}{\Box} \right)$

Use estimation to solve.

5 Tina ran 3.8 miles on Monday, 4.4 miles on Tuesday, and 1.8 miles on Thursday. She says that she ran a total of 15 miles. Is her answer reasonable? Explain.

_____

_____

6 Mei's dog eats 3 times a day. Each time, the dog eats $\frac{3}{4}$ cup of food. Mei says that her dog eats $15\frac{3}{4}$ cups of dog food each week. Is her answer reasonable? Explain.

_____

_____

Solve.

> I can reorder or regroup numbers to make computation easier.

7 A dog weighed 55.48 pounds. Another dog weighed 65.29 pounds. A third dog weighed 4.52 pounds. How many pounds do the dogs weigh in all?

_____

8 A box has a length of 2.5 yards, a width of 1.7 yards, and a height of 0.4 yards. What is the volume of the box? Volume = length × width × height

_____

DISCUSS

Make sense of problems.

On Monday, Susie bought sandwich priced at $7.35 and used coupon for $1.25 off. On Tuesday, she spent $5.75 on a combo meal. Susie wrote this expression to find how much she spent in all.

(7.35 − 1.25) + 5.75

She used the associative property to regroup the expression.

7.35 − (1.25 + 5.75)

> I remember! I have to check the operations in an expression to decide if I can use a number property.

Is Susie correct? Explain. _____

_____

PROBLEM SOLVING

Back to School!

BACK-TO-SCHOOL SHOPPING

READ

Amy plans to buy five sets of clothes for a new school year. For each set, she will buy one shirt for $19.80, one pair of pants for $36.45, and a belt for $14.20. Will $300 be enough for clothes?

PLAN

• What is the problem asking you to find?

   whether $_____ is enough for clothes

• What do you need to know solve the problem?

   Amy will buy __5__ sets of clothing.

   For each set, Amy will spend $_____ on a shirt, $_____ on pants,

   and $ _____ on a belt.

• What expressions can you use to solve the problem?

   __5__ × (_____ + _____ + _____)

SOLVE

Use a number property to add.

_____ × (_____ + _____ + _____)

_____ × (_____ + _____)

__5__ × (_____) = _____

352.25 is _____ than 300.

CHECK

Use estimation.

19.80 is close to _____, 36.45 is close to _____, and 14.20 is

close to _____. Use the estimated numbers.

5 × (_____ + _____ + _____)

5 × (_____) = _____

This is close to my answer of _____.

The clothes will cost Amy _____, so $300 is _____ to buy them all.

> I remember! I can use compatible numbers that are easier to work with.

PRACTICE

Use the problem-solving steps to help you.

I know there are 60 minutes in an hour and 24 hours in a day. I can use these rates to write a multiplication expression.

1 If 150 people are born every minute, how many people are born every day?

CHECKLIST
- [ ] READ
- [ ] PLAN
- [ ] SOLVE
- [ ] CHECK

2 At a track meet, Marshall adds his high jump, long jump, and triple jump distances for a single score. His high jump distance was 1.71 meters. His long jump distance was 5.61 meters. His triple jump distance was 13.29 meters. Last year, his total distance in all three events was 21 meters. How far was he this year from last year's total distance?

CHECKLIST
- [ ] READ
- [ ] PLAN
- [ ] SOLVE
- [ ] CHECK

3 Joanne earns $75 each day. After taxes, she receives $\frac{2}{3}$ of what she earns and then saves $\frac{1}{5}$ of this for college. How much does she save each day for college?

CHECKLIST
- [ ] READ
- [ ] PLAN
- [ ] SOLVE
- [ ] CHECK

Back to School!

103

Solving Multi-Step Real-World Problems

PLUG IN — Solving Single-Step Mathematical Problems with Decimals

The thermometers show the temperatures on Monday and Tuesday. How many degrees higher was Tuesday's temperature than Monday's?

Monday   Tuesday

11.2°F
10°F   10°F
?
0°F   0°F
−5.9°F
−10°F   −10°F

Write an expression to represent the problem.

$$11.2 - (-5.9) = ?$$

You can use the rules for operations with rational numbers to find the answer.
Rewrite as addition.

$$11.2 + 5.9 = 17.1$$

The temperature difference is 17.1°F.

Ok! The temperature is −5.9°F on Monday and 11.2°F on Tuesday.

I remember! Subtracting a number is the same as adding the opposite of that number.

DISCUSS

Can the order of the numbers you subtract change the answer? Explain by comparing $11.2 - (-5.9)$ to $-5.9 - (11.2)$.

A You can solve addition problems with decimals.

DO

A scientist mixes 56.69 grams of one sample with 85.1 grams of another sample. How many grams is the total mixture?

❶ Write an expression to represent the problem.

<u>**56.69**</u> + _____

❷ Add.

_____ + _____ = _____

❸ Write the sum.

The mixture is _____ grams.

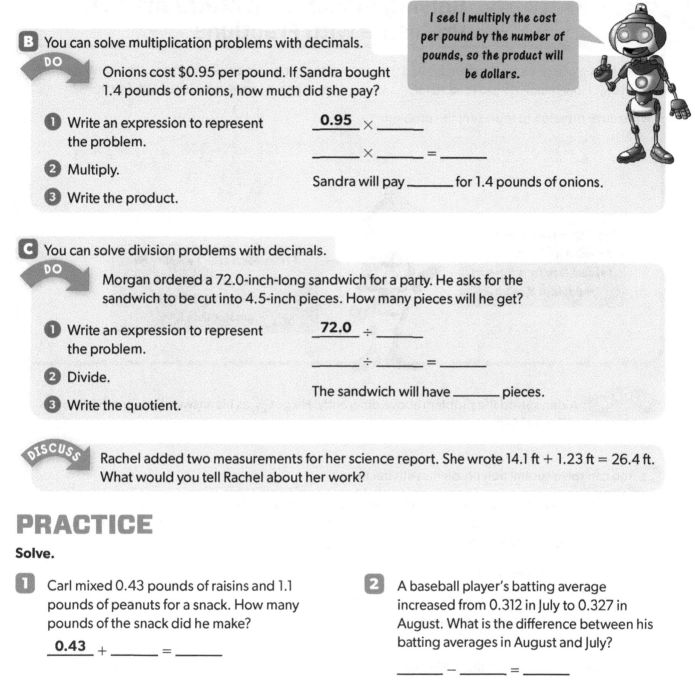

B You can solve multiplication problems with decimals.

DO

Onions cost $0.95 per pound. If Sandra bought 1.4 pounds of onions, how much did she pay?

I see! I multiply the cost per pound by the number of pounds, so the product will be dollars.

❶ Write an expression to represent the problem.

❷ Multiply.

❸ Write the product.

__0.95__ × _____

_____ × _____ = _____

Sandra will pay _____ for 1.4 pounds of onions.

C You can solve division problems with decimals.

DO

Morgan ordered a 72.0-inch-long sandwich for a party. He asks for the sandwich to be cut into 4.5-inch pieces. How many pieces will he get?

❶ Write an expression to represent the problem.

❷ Divide.

❸ Write the quotient.

__72.0__ ÷ _____

_____ ÷ _____ = _____

The sandwich will have _____ pieces.

DISCUSS

Rachel added two measurements for her science report. She wrote 14.1 ft + 1.23 ft = 26.4 ft. What would you tell Rachel about her work?

PRACTICE

Solve.

❶ Carl mixed 0.43 pounds of raisins and 1.1 pounds of peanuts for a snack. How many pounds of the snack did he make?

__0.43__ + _____ = _____

❷ A baseball player's batting average increased from 0.312 in July to 0.327 in August. What is the difference between his batting averages in August and July?

_____ − _____ = _____

❸ A child ticket for the amusement park is 0.45 times the cost of an adult ticket. If an adult ticket costs $20.00, how much does a child ticket cost?

$_____ × _____ = $_____

❹ A pack of snack cakes weighs 13.5 ounces. If each cake weighs 1.125 ounces, how many cakes are in the pack?

_____ ÷ _____ = _____

Solving Single-Step Mathematical Problems with Fractions

Tessa read $\frac{3}{8}$ of a book on Wednesday and $\frac{1}{6}$ on Thursday. How much has she read so far?

Write an expression to represent the problem.

$$\frac{3}{8} + \frac{1}{6}$$

You can use the rules for operations with rational numbers to solve problems with fractions.

$$\frac{3}{8} + \frac{1}{6}$$

$$\frac{3}{8} \times \frac{3}{3} = \frac{9}{24} \qquad \frac{1}{6} \times \frac{4}{4} = \frac{4}{24}$$

$$\frac{9}{24} + \frac{4}{24} = \frac{13}{24}$$

Tessa has read $\frac{13}{24}$ of the book so far.

> The fractions have different denominators, so I should look for a common multiple of 8 and 6.

> I remember! I can't simplify my answer further because 13 and 24 do not have a common factor greater than 1.

DISCUSS Aiden solved the problem above differently. He got $\frac{26}{48}$ as his answer. Why are the answers different? Explain.

A You can solve subtraction problems with fractions.

DO

A farmer saw that a tomato plant in the shade grew $\frac{1}{3}$ foot in a week. She also saw that a tomato plant in the sun grew $\frac{3}{4}$ foot in the same week. What is the difference between the amounts the plants grew?

1. Write an expression to represent the problem.

2. Rewrite the fractions with common denominators.

3. Subtract the new fractions. Simplify if necessary.

4. Write the difference.

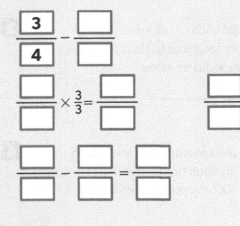

The difference is _____ foot.

I rewrite the division problem of fractions as multiplication by the reciprocal of the divisor.

B You can solve division problems with fractions.

DO

Franklin split $\frac{5}{6}$ pound of peanuts into $\frac{1}{9}$-pound snack bags. How many snack bags did he make?

1 Write an expression to represent the problem.

2 Rewrite the division expression as a multiplication expression.

3 Multiply. Simplify if necessary.

4 Write the quotient.

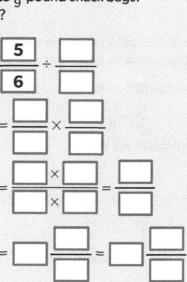

Franklin made _____ snack bags.

DISCUSS

Phil says he prefers to work with decimals rather than with fractions. Use the example above to explain why it is important to be able to work with fractions, too.

PRACTICE

Solve. Simplify, if necessary.

1 Alana's scuba tank was $\frac{9}{10}$ full before her dive and $\frac{2}{5}$ full after her dive. How much of the air in the tank did she use on her dive?

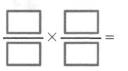

2 Ursula mowed $\frac{2}{3}$ of the lawn. Her sister mowed $\frac{2}{9}$ of the lawn. How much of the lawn did they mow together?

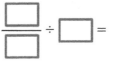

3 Nick planned to complete $\frac{2}{3}$ of his chores today. Of those, he was going to complete $\frac{3}{4}$ before dinner. How much of his chores will he complete before dinner today?

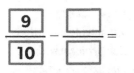

4 Carrie has $\frac{2}{3}$ yard of ribbon. She will cut the ribbon into 4 equal pieces. What will be the length for each piece of ribbon?

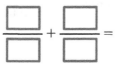

Solving Multi-Step Real-World Problems

You can solve a multi-step real-world problem by using the following steps:

Emmett sent $\frac{1}{8}$ of his 16 postcards to family. He sent $\frac{5}{7}$ of the rest to friends. How many postcards did he send to friends?

Step 1: Find how many postcards Emmett sent to his family.

$$\frac{1}{8} \text{ of } 16 = \frac{1}{8} \times 16 = \frac{1}{8} \times \frac{16}{1} = \frac{1 \times 16}{8 \times 1} = \frac{16}{8} = 2$$

Step 2: Find how many postcards are left.

$$16 - 2 = 14$$

Step 3: Find how many cards Emmett sent to his friends.

$$\frac{5}{7} \text{ of } 14 = \frac{5}{7} \times 14 = \frac{5}{7} \times \frac{14}{1} = \frac{5 \times 14}{7 \times 1} = \frac{70}{7} = 10$$

Emmett sent 2 postcards to his family and 10 postcards to his friends.

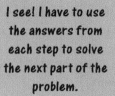

I see! I have to use the answers from each step to solve the next part of the problem.

DISCUSS Jeanine tried to solve the problem in one step. She multiplied $16 \times \frac{1}{8} \times \frac{5}{7}$. She was confused that her answer was a fraction. What would you tell Jeanine about her work?

LESSON LINK

PLUG IN	POWER UP	GO!

You can solve single-step problems with decimals.

If there are 2.54 centimeters per inch, how many centimeters are in 2.7 inches?

$$
\begin{array}{r}
2.54 \\
\times\ 2.7 \\
\hline
1\ 778 \\
5\ 080 \\
\hline
6.858
\end{array}
$$

There are 6.858 centimeters in 2.7 inches.

You can solve single-step problems with fractions.

If $\frac{1}{9}$ of Irene's kittens are gray and $\frac{2}{3}$ are white, how many of her kittens are gray or white?

$$\frac{1}{9} + \frac{2}{3}$$
$$= \frac{1}{9} + \frac{6}{9} = \frac{7}{9}$$

$\frac{7}{9}$ of Irene's kittens are gray or white.

I see! I can think about solving a multi-step problem with decimals or fractions as solving a series of single-step problems.

WORK TOGETHER

You can solve multi-step problems by planning and solving one step at a time.

Step 1: Subtract the amount left over from the amount raised.

The T-shirts cost $126.50 in all.

Step 2: Divide the answer from Step 1 by the number of people on the team.

The T-shirts cost $11.50 per person.

The cheerleading team raised $143.26 to buy T-shirts and had $16.76 left over. If there are 11 people on the team, what is the cost per person for the T-shirts?

Remember to align the decimal points when subtracting!

Step 1	Step 2
12	11.50
3̶2̶ 12	11)126.50
14̶3̶.2̶6̶	−11
− 16.76	16
126.50	−11
	55
	−55
	00

A You can solve multi-step problems with fractions.

DO

While walking to school, Patrice saw that $\frac{1}{12}$ of the cars that passed had one person in them and $\frac{1}{8}$ had two people. If Patrice was passed by 24 cars in all, how many have three or more people in them?

❶ Write an expression to represent the fraction of the cars that had one or two people.

$$\frac{\square}{\square} + \frac{\square}{\square}$$

❷ Write equivalent fractions with common denominators.

$$\frac{\square}{\square} \times \frac{2}{2} = \frac{\square}{\square} \qquad \frac{\square}{\square} \times \frac{3}{3} = \frac{\square}{\square}$$

❸ Add the new fractions.

❹ Write an expression to represent the number of cars that had one or two people.

$$\frac{\square}{\square} + \frac{\square}{\square} = \frac{\square}{\square}$$

❺ Write the whole number as a fraction. Multiply and find the product.

$$\frac{\square}{\square} \times 24 = \frac{\square}{\square} \times \frac{\square}{\square} = \frac{\square}{\square} = \underline{\quad}$$

❻ Subtract that number from 24.

$$24 - \underline{\quad} = \underline{\quad}$$

❼ Write the answer.

There were _____ cars that have three or more people.

DISCUSS

Explain how you can check the answer in the problem above.

PRACTICE

Work through each step to solve the problem.

1 Lyle made $2\frac{1}{3}$ dozen pancakes. Randy took $\frac{1}{7}$ of them and Matt took $\frac{2}{7}$ of the pancakes. How many pancakes are left over?

Find how many pancakes Lyle made.

$$\underline{\quad 2\frac{1}{3} \quad} \times \underline{\quad 12 \quad} = \underline{\qquad}$$

Find how many pancakes each person took.

Randy = _____ × _____ = _____   Matt = _____ × _____ = _____

Find how many pancakes in all Randy and Matt took.

_____ + _____ = _____

Find how many pancakes are left over.

_____ − _____ = _____

2 Kelly's two suitcases have the same weight. Together, they weigh $100\frac{1}{5}$ pounds. If she removes $5\frac{3}{10}$ pounds of baggage from each suitcase, what is the final weight of each suitcase?

Find the original weight of each suitcase.

_____ ÷ _____ = _____ pounds

Find the final weight of each suitcase.

_____ − _____ = _____ pounds

3 Graciela has 2 quarters and 3 dimes in her pocket. The total weight of the coins is 18.144 grams. If each quarter weighs 5.670 grams, how much does each dime weigh?

Find the total weight of the quarters.

_____ × _____ = _____ grams

Find the total weight of the dimes.

_____ − _____ = _____ grams

Find the weight of each dime.

_____ ÷ _____ = _____ grams

Solve each step to solve the problem.

4 The world record for the men's 100-meter dash, set in 2009, is 9.58 seconds. The world record in 1964 was $\frac{12}{25}$ second greater than the world record in 2009. If the world record in 1991 was 0.2 second less than the world record in 1964, what was the world record in 1991?

Find the world record in 1964. _____ seconds

Find the world record in 1991. _____ seconds

5 The world record in 1974 for the women's 200-meter dash was 22.21 seconds. The world record in 1979 was 0.5 second less than in 1974. The world record set in 1988 is $\frac{37}{100}$ second less than in 1979. What was the record set in 1988?

Find the world record in 1979. _____ seconds

Find the world record in 1988. _____ seconds

> I get it! I have to find and solve each step to solve the next step.

Solve.

6 A school chorus is made up of sixth, seventh, and eighth graders. Two-sevenths of the chorus are sixth graders. There are 1.5 times as many seventh graders as sixth graders. If there are 175 members in the chorus, how many are eighth graders? _____

7 Diamond weight is measured in carets. The Hope Diamond originally had a weight of $112\frac{3}{16}$ carats, but $45\frac{1}{16}$ carats were removed in 1673. The Hope Diamond now weighs 21.605 carats less than it did in 1673. Write its current weight as a decimal. _____

DISCUSS

Different Ways to Solve a Problem

Rachel and Vera have baked 36 cookies and are giving $\frac{1}{3}$ to the family, $\frac{2}{9}$ to neighbors, and the rest to co-workers.

To figure out how many cookies to give to co-workers, Rachel wrote this expression:

$36 - \left(36 \times \frac{1}{3} + 36 \times \frac{2}{9}\right)$

Vera wrote this expression:

$36 \times \left[1 - \left(\frac{1}{3} + \frac{2}{9}\right)\right]$

Who is correct?

> I see! Sometimes there is more than one way to solve a problem.

How many cookies will they give to co-workers?

PROBLEM SOLVING

ROAD TRIP PLANNING

READ Zahra's car has a gas tank that holds $13\frac{1}{3}$ gallons. Her car can travel 22.8 miles per gallon of gas. How many tanks of gas would she need to drive 364.8 miles? Show your answer as a mixed number.

PLAN
- What is the problem asking you to find?

  the number of _____ of gas Zahra needs for her trip

- What do you need to know to solve the problem?

  Zahra needs to travel _____ miles.

  Her car can travel _____ miles per gallon, and the gas tank holds _____ gallons.

- How can you solve the problem?

  Divide 364.8 by 22.8 to find the amount of gas Zehra needs.

  Then divide that quotient by $13\frac{1}{3}$ to find the number of tanks of gas.

SOLVE Find the amount of gas she needs.

_____ ÷ _____ = _____ gallons

Find the number of tanks she needs.

_____ ÷ _____ = _____

CHECK Use multiplication to check division.

Multiply the number of tanks needed by the number of gallons the tank holds.

_____ × _____ = _____

> I remember! Dividing by a fraction is the same as multiplying by its reciprocal.

Multiply the number of gallons by miles per gallon.

_____ × _____ = _____

Zahra will need _____ tanks of gas.

PRACTICE

Use the problem-solving steps to help you.

1 Lucia has a flash drive that is $\frac{7}{10}$ full and can hold 2 GB of data. Lucia adds three more data files that are 0.094 GB, 0.336 GB, and 0.112 GB. How many more GB can fit on the flash drive?

CHECKLIST
- [ ] READ
- [ ] PLAN
- [ ] SOLVE
- [ ] CHECK

2 The distance between the basement floor and first floor in Andrew's house is $7\frac{1}{4}$ feet. The distance between the first floor and the second floor is $1\frac{1}{2}$ feet greater. The house has a stairway from the basement to the second floor.
If each step is 0.5 feet tall, how many steps (including the top step) are in this stairway?

CHECKLIST
- [ ] READ
- [ ] PLAN
- [ ] SOLVE
- [ ] CHECK

3 Neither the moon nor Earth is a perfect sphere. On the moon, the distance from pole to pole is 3,472 km, while the distance along the equator is 3,476.2 km. On Earth, the distance from pole to pole is 12,713.6 km, while the distance along the equator is 12,756.2 km. How much larger is the difference between the equator measure and the pole-to-pole measure on Earth than it is on the moon?

I get it! First, I need to find the difference between the distances on Earth. Then, I need to find the difference between the distances on the moon, Last, I need to find the difference between those numbers.

CHECKLIST
- [ ] READ
- [ ] PLAN
- [ ] SOLVE
- [ ] CHECK

Solving Word Problems Algebraically

PLUG IN Solving One-Step Algebraic Equations

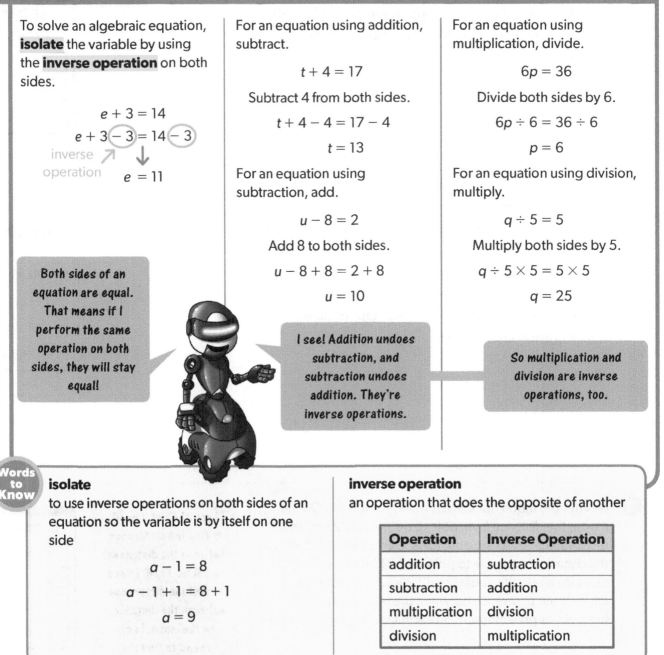

To solve an algebraic equation, **isolate** the variable by using the **inverse operation** on both sides.

$$e + 3 = 14$$
$$e + 3 - 3 = 14 - 3$$
inverse operation
$$e = 11$$

For an equation using addition, subtract.

$$t + 4 = 17$$

Subtract 4 from both sides.

$$t + 4 - 4 = 17 - 4$$
$$t = 13$$

For an equation using subtraction, add.

$$u - 8 = 2$$

Add 8 to both sides.

$$u - 8 + 8 = 2 + 8$$
$$u = 10$$

For an equation using multiplication, divide.

$$6p = 36$$

Divide both sides by 6.

$$6p \div 6 = 36 \div 6$$
$$p = 6$$

For an equation using division, multiply.

$$q \div 5 = 5$$

Multiply both sides by 5.

$$q \div 5 \times 5 = 5 \times 5$$
$$q = 25$$

Both sides of an equation are equal. That means if I perform the same operation on both sides, they will stay equal!

I see! Addition undoes subtraction, and subtraction undoes addition. They're inverse operations.

So multiplication and division are inverse operations, too.

Words to Know

isolate
to use inverse operations on both sides of an equation so the variable is by itself on one side

$$a - 1 = 8$$
$$a - 1 + 1 = 8 + 1$$
$$a = 9$$

inverse operation
an operation that does the opposite of another

Operation	Inverse Operation
addition	subtraction
subtraction	addition
multiplication	division
division	multiplication

DISCUSS Dani says that the equations $j + 7 = 12$ and $7 + j = 12$ cannot be solved the same way. What can you tell her about her reasoning?

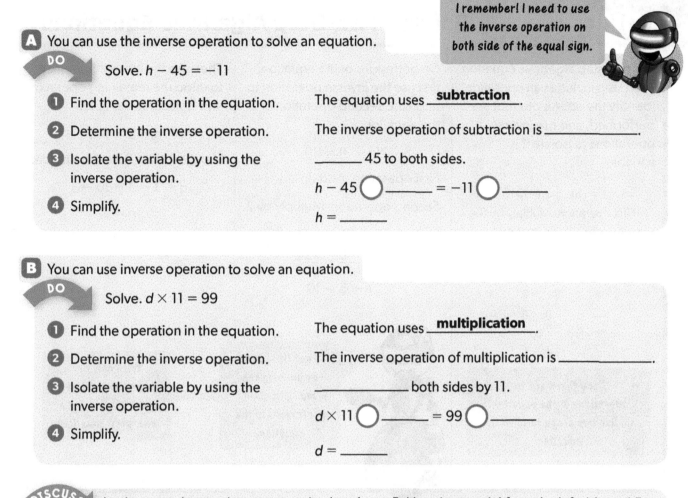

A You can use the inverse operation to solve an equation.

I remember! I need to use the inverse operation on both side of the equal sign.

DO Solve. $h - 45 = -11$

1 Find the operation in the equation. The equation uses ___**subtraction**___.

2 Determine the inverse operation. The inverse operation of subtraction is _____.

3 Isolate the variable by using the inverse operation. _____ 45 to both sides.

$h - 45 \bigcirc \underline{\hspace{1cm}} = -11 \bigcirc \underline{\hspace{1cm}}$

4 Simplify. $h = \underline{\hspace{1cm}}$

B You can use inverse operation to solve an equation.

DO Solve. $d \times 11 = 99$

1 Find the operation in the equation. The equation uses ___**multiplication**___.

2 Determine the inverse operation. The inverse operation of multiplication is _____.

3 Isolate the variable by using the inverse operation. _____ both sides by 11.

$d \times 11 \bigcirc \underline{\hspace{1cm}} = 99 \bigcirc \underline{\hspace{1cm}}$

4 Simplify. $d = \underline{\hspace{1cm}}$

DISCUSS Justin wanted to use inverses to solve $k + 4 = -5$. He subtracted 4 from the left side and 5 from the right side. What can you tell him about his method?

PRACTICE

Solve each equation.

1 $y + 2 = 7$

$y + 2 - \underline{\hspace{0.5cm}2\hspace{0.5cm}} = 7 - \underline{\hspace{1cm}}$

$y = \underline{\hspace{1cm}}$

2 $s - 6 = 8$

$s - 6 + \underline{\hspace{1cm}} = 8 + \underline{\hspace{1cm}}$

$s = \underline{\hspace{1cm}}$

3 $12n = 48$

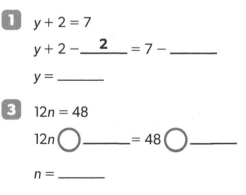

$12n \bigcirc \underline{\hspace{1cm}} = 48 \bigcirc \underline{\hspace{1cm}}$

$n = \underline{\hspace{1cm}}$

4 $w \div 9 = 9$

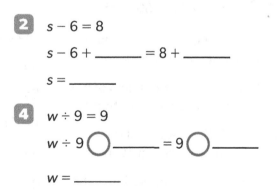

$w \div 9 \bigcirc \underline{\hspace{1cm}} = 9 \bigcirc \underline{\hspace{1cm}}$

$w = \underline{\hspace{1cm}}$

Solving Two-Step Algebraic Equations

In a two-step algebraic equation, each step includes an operation. Identify the operations that are performed, and use inverse operations to isolate the variable.

$$8v + 5 = 13$$

First operation: Multiply by 8.
Second operation: Add 5.

$$8v + 5 \boxed{-5} = 13 \boxed{-5}$$

inverse ↗ ↓
operation $8v = 8$

$$8v \boxed{\div 8} = 8 \boxed{\div 8}$$

inverse ↗ ↓
operation $v = 1$

Since there are two operations in the equation, I'll use two steps to solve the equation.

On both sides of the equation, first use the inverse operation to undo the second operation of the equation.

$$2(n + 3) = 20$$

First operation: Add 3.

Second operation: Multiply by 2.

First, divide both sides by 2.

$$\frac{2(n + 3)}{2} = \frac{20}{2}$$

$$n + 3 = 10$$

I get it! I start by undoing the multiplication performed in the equation.

Then use the inverse operation to undo the remaining operation and isolate the variable.

$$n + 3 = 10$$

Next, subtract 3 from both sides.

$$n + 3 - 3 = 10 - 3$$

$$n = 7$$

With only one operation left, it's just like solving a one-step equation!

DISCUSS How can you check your answer when you solve an equation?

A You can use inverse operations to solve two-step equations.

DO
Solve. $5q - 50 = 25$

1 Identify the second operation performed in the equation.

2 Use the inverse operation of the second operation on both sides.

3 Identify the first operation performed in the equation.

4 Use the inverse operation of the remaining operation to isolate the variable.

The second operation performed is _____.

$$5q - 50 \boxed{+} \underline{\textbf{50}} = 25 \bigcirc \underline{\hphantom{xx}}$$

$$5q = \underline{\hphantom{xx}}$$

The first operation performed is _____.

$$5q \bigcirc \underline{\hphantom{xx}} = \underline{\hphantom{xx}} \bigcirc \underline{\hphantom{xx}}$$

$$q = \underline{\hphantom{xx}}$$

B You can use inverse operations to solve two-step equations.

> I remember! $\frac{g-8}{5}$ is equivalent to $(g-8) \div 5!$

DO Solve. $\frac{g-8}{5} = -13$

1 Identify the second operation performed in the equation.

2 Use the inverse operation of the second operation on both sides.

3 Identify the first operation performed in the equation.

4 Use the inverse operation of the remaining operation to isolate the variable.

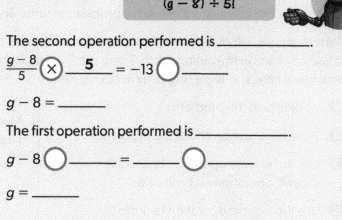

The second operation performed is _____.

$\frac{g-8}{5} \,\bigotimes\, \underline{\quad 5 \quad} = -13 \bigcirc \underline{\qquad}$

$g - 8 = \underline{\qquad}$

The first operation performed is _____.

$g - 8 \bigcirc \underline{\qquad} = \underline{\qquad} \bigcirc \underline{\qquad}$

$g = \underline{\qquad}$

DISCUSS Jane solved the equation $\frac{s}{4} + 3 = 9$. Her work is shown below.

$$\frac{s}{4} + 3 = 9$$

$$\frac{s}{4} + 3 - 3 = 9 - 3$$

$$\frac{s}{4} = 6$$

$$\frac{s}{4} \div 4 = 6 \div 4$$

$$s = 1\frac{1}{2}$$

Is Jane's work correct? If not, what is the correct answer?

PRACTICE

Solve the equation.

1 $12(f - 15) = 144$

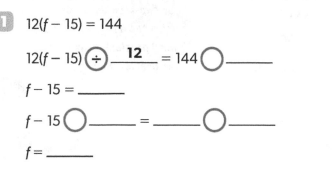

$12(f - 15) \,\bigodiv\, \underline{\quad 12 \quad} = 144 \bigcirc \underline{\qquad}$

$f - 15 = \underline{\qquad}$

$f - 15 \bigcirc \underline{\qquad} = \underline{\qquad} \bigcirc \underline{\qquad}$

$f = \underline{\qquad}$

2 $\frac{d + 22}{5} = 6$

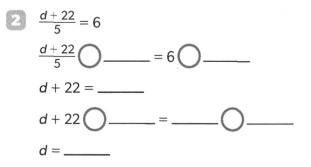

$\frac{d + 22}{5} \bigcirc \underline{\qquad} = 6 \bigcirc \underline{\qquad}$

$d + 22 = \underline{\qquad}$

$d + 22 \bigcirc \underline{\qquad} = \underline{\qquad} \bigcirc \underline{\qquad}$

$d = \underline{\qquad}$

You can use the information given in a problem to write and solve an equation.

Manesh moves half of the chairs from the kitchen into the dining room. There were already 5 chairs in the dining room. There are 9 chairs in the dining room now. How many chairs, k, were originally in the kitchen?

1. Understand the problem.

2. Write an equation about the problem.

3. Use the inverse operation to undo the second operation on both sides.

4. Use the inverse operation to undo the remaining operation to isolate the variable.

There were originally 8 chairs in the kitchen.

The dining room originally had 5 chairs. Manesh adds half of the kitchen chairs, or $\frac{k}{2}$. The dining room now has a total of 9 chairs.

$$\frac{k}{2} + 5 = 9$$

$$\frac{k}{2} + 5 - 5 = 9 - 5$$

$$\frac{k}{2} = 4$$

$$\frac{k}{2} \times 2 = 4 \times 2$$

$$k = 8$$

Dividing by 2 is the same as taking half, and adding 5 gives me the total number of chairs in the dining room.

 DISCUSS Elizabeth tried to solve the problem by multiplying first. $\frac{k}{2} \times 2 + 5 = 9 \times 2$. Will she get the correct answer? Explain.

LESSON LINK

PLUG IN	POWER UP	GO!
Solve one-step algebraic equations by using inverse operations.	Solve two-step algebraic equations by using inverse operations, one at a time.	I see! If I can write a one- or two-step equation by using the information in a word problem, I can solve the problem algebraically.

PLUG IN

$$t - 5 = 0$$
$$t - 5 + 5 = 0 + 5$$
$$t = 5$$

POWER UP

$$7u + 6 = -50$$
$$7u + 6 - 6 = -50 - 6$$
$$7u = -56$$
$$7u \div 7 = -56 \div 7$$
$$u = -8$$

Because the books are split evenly, I add the number of books collected and then divide the total by 3.

WORK TOGETHER

You can write an equation to represent a word problem and solve the problem algebraically.

- The total number of books collected is $34 + z$.

- The books are divided equally among 3 libraries.

- Each library gets 25 books.

- The equation $\frac{(34 + z)}{5} = 5$ represents the problem.

- Solve the equation.

Mr. Zheng's class collects 41 books.

For library week, Ms. Garcia's class collects 34 books and Mr. Zheng's class collects z books. These books are divided equally among 3 local libraries. If each library receives 25 books, how many books does Mr. Zheng's class collect?

$$\frac{(34 + z)}{3} = 25$$

$$\frac{34 + z}{3} \times 3 = 25 \times 3$$

$$34 + z = 75$$

$$34 + z - 34 = 75 - 34$$

$$z = 41$$

A Write an equation and solve the word problem.

DO

Claudette made 4 muffins for each of her cousins and 1 muffin for each of her 20 co-workers. If she made 52 muffins in all, how many cousins, c, does she have?

1. Understand the problem.

2. Write an equation to represent the problem.

3. Solve the equation. Write the value for c.

4. Write the answer.

Claudette made $c \times$ _____ muffins for her cousins.

She made _____ muffin(s) for each of her _____ co-workers.

She made _____ muffins total.

$(c \times$ _____$) +$ _____ $=$ _____

Solve for c.

$(c \times$ _____$) +$ _____ $-$ _____ $=$ _____ $-$ _____

$c \times$ _____ $=$ _____

$c \times$ _____ $\div$ _____ $=$ _____ $\div$ _____

$c =$ _____

Claudette has _____ cousins.

DISCUSS

Each person in Estela's family has 3 jackets in the hall closet. A visiting friend also put a jacket in the closet. There are 13 jackets in the closet. Estela writes the equation $3(f + 1) = 13$ for the number of jackets in the closet, where f is the number of people in her family. What can you tell Estela about her equation?

PRACTICE

Write an equation to represent the problem. Solve.

1 An online greeting card lets you type 30 characters per line on *d* lines and 20 characters on the last line for each message. If the total number of characters for each message is 200, how many lines, *d*, can you type?

$$\underline{\quad 30 \quad} \times d + \underline{\qquad\qquad} = \underline{\quad 200 \quad}$$

2 Ting divides *a* apple slices equally into 5 bags and adds 1 orange slice to each bag. If each bag has 11 slices of fruit, how many apple slices, *a*, does Ting use?

$$\dfrac{a}{\boxed{}} + \underline{\qquad\qquad} = \underline{\qquad\qquad}$$

3 Angel hangs 5 posters and *f* flyers for basketball tryouts around the school, using 4 thumbtacks for each one. If he uses 100 thumbtacks total, how many flyers, *f*, does Angel hang?

$$\underline{\qquad\qquad} \times (f + \underline{\quad 5 \quad}) = \underline{\qquad\qquad}$$

4 During a debate competition, each of 8 students from South High School and *t* students from North High School gives a 5-minute speech. If the total time for all of the students' speeches is 85 minutes, how many students from North High School, *t*, give speeches?

$$\underline{\qquad\qquad} \times (t + \underline{\qquad\qquad}) = \underline{\qquad\qquad}$$

Write an equation. Solve.

5 A hotel puts 4 pillows in each of its *r* rooms and stores another 100 pillows in case guests want more. If the hotel has 452 pillows total, how many rooms, *r*, are in the hotel?

(_____ × _____) + _____ = _____

6 A city plants *t* trees. Forty trees are planted next to streets and the rest are divided equally between 8 parks. If each park gets 25 trees, how many trees, *t*, does the city plant?

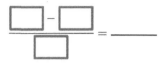

$$\frac{\boxed{} - \boxed{}}{\boxed{}} = \underline{}$$

Solve.

7 A newsstand displays *m* magazines and 50 newspapers. They are divided equally among 4 shelves. If each shelf has 30 magazines and newspapers, what is the value of *m*?

_____

> I remember! I have to write an expression for the total number of magazines and newspapers first!

8 Adrienne makes a pitcher of 12 cups of lemonade. She pours *c* cups of lemonade for each of 5 friends. If there are 2 cups left in the pitcher, what is the value of *c*?

_____

DISCUSS

Different Equations for One Word Problem

A carpenter uses 3 hinges to put up a door. He puts up 4 doors on the first floor and *s* doors on the second floor. If he uses 27 hinges total, what is the value of *s*?

The carpenter writes the equations $4 + 3s = 27$ and $3(4 + s) = 27$, but he can't decide which is correct. What would you tell him?

How many doors, *s*, are on the second floor?

> By the distributive property, I know $3(4 + s) = 27$ is equal to $12 + 3s = 27$. So I know this equation is not equal to $4 + 3s + 27$.

PROBLEM SOLVING

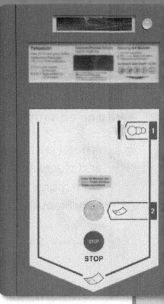

PARKING PAYMENT

READ

Lauren parks in a garage that charges $6 for the first hour and n dollars for each additional hour. If she paid a total of $22 for 5 hours of parking, what is the charge for each additional hour of parking?

PLAN

• What is the problem asking you to find?

the cost of each hour of parking after the __first__ hour

• What do you need to know to solve the problem?

The garage charges $ _____ for the first hour.

Lauren paid $ _____ for _____ hours of parking.

• What equation will you use to solve the problem?

_____ + _____ × n = _____

SOLVE

Solve the equation for n.

_____ + _____ × n = _____

_____ ◯ _____ + _____ × n = _____ ◯ _____

_____ × n = _____

_____ × n ◯ _____ = _____ ◯ _____

n = _____

CHECK

Substitute the value of n into the original equation.

_____ + _____ × n = _____

_____ + _____ × _____ = _____

_____ + _____ = _____

_____ = _____

The charge for each hour of parking after the first hour is $_____ .

> I see! Lauren paid $6 for the first hour and n dollars for each of the remaining 4 hours.

PRACTICE

Use the problem-solving steps to help you.

1 During a sale, the first DVD purchased costs $19, and each additional DVD purchased costs *d* dollars. If Javier buys 4 DVDs and spends a total of $58, how much does each additional DVD cost, *d*?

To write an equation, I must count the number of additional DVDs. There are 4 — 1, or 3, of them.

CHECKLIST
- [ ] READ
- [ ] PLAN
- [ ] SOLVE
- [ ] CHECK

2 A restaurant has *r* reservations each hour except its last hour, when it has 5 reservations. If the restaurant is open for 6 hours and has a total of 55 reservations, how many reservations, *r*, does the restaurant have each hour?

CHECKLIST
- [ ] READ
- [ ] PLAN
- [ ] SOLVE
- [ ] CHECK

3 A movie theater shows *m* movies each day from Monday through Friday. On Saturday and Sunday, the theater shows 48 movies each day. If the theater shows 256 movies each week, how many movies, *m*, does the theater show from Monday through Friday?

CHECKLIST
- [ ] READ
- [ ] PLAN
- [ ] SOLVE
- [ ] CHECK

Using Inequalities to Solve Problems

PLUG IN   Solving One-Step Inequalities

An **inequality** is a sentence that shows one quantity is less than or greater than the other.

$$13 - 4 > 5 + 2$$
$$2 \times 3 < 81 \div 9$$

The **solution set** of an inequality with a variable is a set of numbers.

$$x > 4$$
$$y < -30$$

I see! The symbols $<$ and $>$ are used when the expressions are not equal.

You can use inequalities to represent problems.

Carnival tickets cost $5 each. Write an inequality to find the number of tickets you can buy with $25.

Let t represent the number of tickets. With $25, the product of 5 and t must be less than or equal to $25.

$$5t \leq 25$$

I get it! The inequality indicates which values of t make the statement true.

Use properties of operations to solve inequalities.

Undo multiplication with the inverse operation, division.

$$5t \leq 25$$
$$5t \div 5 \leq 25 \div 5$$
$$t \leq 5$$

You can buy 5 or fewer tickets with $25.

I see! Solving an inequality is similar to solving an equation.

Words to Know

inequality
a comparison of two expressions that uses one of these signs: $<$ (less than), $>$ (greater than), $\leq$ (less than or equal to), $\geq$ (greater than or equal to), or $\neq$ (not equal)

solution set
the solution of all numbers that make an inequality true

DISCUSS   Why is the symbol $\leq$ used rather than $<$? Explain.

A You can solve inequalities by using inverse operations.

DO   Solve $-7x < 49$ for x. $7x < 49$

❶ Undo multiplication by the inverse operation.

$$7x \div \underline{\quad 7 \quad} < 49 \bigcirc \underline{\qquad}$$

$$x < \underline{\qquad}$$

❷ Write the solution set.

The solution set is any value that is less than _____.

❸ Check your answer. Replace x with a value from the solution set.

Check. Let $x = 6$.

$$7 \times 6 < 49$$

$$\underline{\qquad} < 49$$

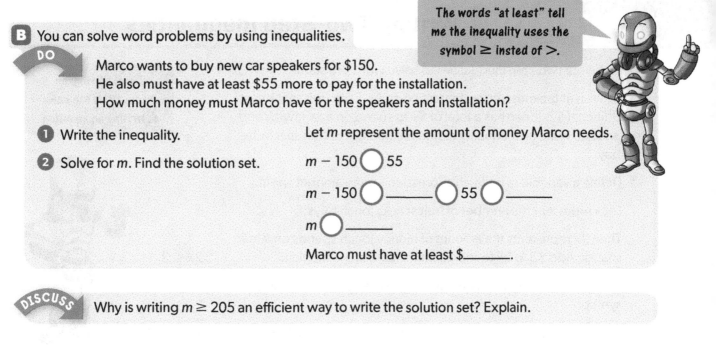

B You can solve word problems by using inequalities.

The words "at least" tell me the inequality uses the symbol ≥ insted of >.

DO

Marco wants to buy new car speakers for $150.
He also must have at least $55 more to pay for the installation.
How much money must Marco have for the speakers and installation?

1 Write the inequality.

2 Solve for *m*. Find the solution set.

Let *m* represent the amount of money Marco needs.

$m - 150 \bigcirc 55$

$m - 150 \bigcirc \underline{\quad} \bigcirc 55 \bigcirc \underline{\quad}$

$m \bigcirc \underline{\quad}$

Marco must have at least $\underline{\quad}$.

DISCUSS

Why is writing $m \geq 205$ an efficient way to write the solution set? Explain.

PRACTICE

Solve each inequality.

1 $2x < 10$

_____

2 $5y \geq 15$

_____

3 $m - 8 < 56$

_____

4 $13 + x > 35$

_____

Write an inequality to represent each problem. Then solve.

5 Cheryl has $14 to spend on apples for baking apple pies. How many pounds, *p*, of apples can she buy if 1 pound costs $2?

_____

6 Kareem had saved *a* dollars from his weekly allowance. After he spent $35 on a video game, Kareem had less than $25 left over. How much money had Kareem saved?

_____

7 Jamie has a 24-ounce bottle of water. His drinking cup holds 8 ounces. How many cups, *c*, of water can he pour without drinking all the water in the bottle?

_____

8 Cara has 115 marbles in her collection. If she wants to acquire at least 275 marbles by the end of the year, how many more marbles, *m*, does she need?

_____

POWER UP Writing Two-Step Inequalities

You can write two-step inequalities to solve word problems.

A sandwich at the museum restaurant costs $3. Each fruit snack costs an additional $2. Jonah has a total of $9 to spend on a sandwich and fruit snacks. Write an inequality to find the number of fruit snacks he can buy.

> I see! Writing an inequality is the same as writing an equation.

1 Define a variable to write an expression for the amount spent.

Let x represent the number of fruit snacks Jonah buys.

Then $2x$ represents the amount of money Jonah spends on x fruit snacks. Add $3 to $2x$ to represent the cost of a sandwich.

$$2x + 3$$

2 Write an expression for comparison, and select the inequality symbol.

The total amount of money Jonah spends, $(2x + 3)$, must be less than or equal to the total amount of money Jonah has, (9).

$$2x + 3 \le 9$$

DISCUSS In what situation would the correct inequality for Jonah have been $2x + 3 \ge 9$?

A Word problems can be shown with two-step inequalities.

DO

Erin makes $8 an hour at her job. She also makes $35 per week in tips. How many hours must she work in order to make at least $200 in one week. Write an inequality to represent this problem.

1 Define a variable.

Let h represent the number of hours Erin must work.

2 Write an expression to find how much Erin earns in 8 hours.

$$\underline{\quad\quad}\,\underline{h}$$

3 Add $35 to that product. This represents how much Erin earns per week.

$$\underline{\quad\quad}\,\underline{h} + \underline{\quad\quad}$$

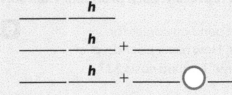

4 Complete the inequality that represents "at least $200."

$$\underline{\quad\quad}\,\underline{h} + \underline{\quad\quad}\,\bigcirc\,\underline{\quad\quad}$$

> Writing an inequality expression is just like writing an equation, but there are no equal signs!

B You can write an inequality to represent a situation.

DO

To receive a grade of a B or better, Pam must have an average of 85 or more on her two exams. Her score on the first exam was an 82. Write an inequality representing the score that Pam must get on her second exam to receive a final grade of a B.

1 Define a variable.

Let x represent Pam's score on the second exam.

2 Write an expression that represents the sum of both exams.

3 Divide the sum by the number of tests. This represents the average of the two exams.

4 Complete the inequality that represents "85 or more."

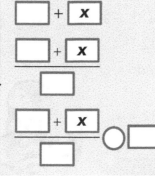

DISCUSS

What information does the inequality used in the previous problem tell you that an equation would not?

PRACTICE

Write an inequality to represent each situation.

1 At one café, the cost for a laptop Internet connection is $0.25 plus an additional $0.05 per minute. Write an inequality to show the number of minutes a person can have an Internet connection so that the cost is no more than $3.

Let *m* represent the number of minutes after the first minute.

_____

2 The length of a rectangle is 100 centimeters, and its perimeter is greater than 200 centimeters. Write an inequality to find the width of the rectangle.

Let *w* represent the width of the rectangle.

_____

3 A taxi service charges $2.75 plus an additional $0.70 per mile. Toby has $20 to spend on a ride. Write an inequality to find the number of miles Toby can travel.

Let *m* represent the number of miles.

_____

Using Inequalities to Solve Problems

You can solve a two-step inequality by using inverse operations on both sides.

Solve $4x + 3 \le 15$ for x.

Subtract 3 from both sides to undo addition.

$$4x + 3 - 3 \le 15 - 3$$

$$4x \le 12$$

Divide both sides by 4 to undo multiplication.

$$4x \div 4 \le 12 \div 4$$

$$x \le 3$$

You can show the solution set for an inequality on a number line.

The solution set is any number less than or equal to 3.

To show that 3 is part of the solution set, draw a closed circle at 3.

To show that numbers less than 3 are in the solution set, shade the part to the left of 3.

I get it! I find the operations in the inequality, then I undo them one step at a time.

I see! A closed circle shows that a number is included in the solution set. An open circle shows that a number is not included.

DISCUSS   How would you shade the number line differently if the inequality was $x > 3$ rather than $x \le 3$?

LESSON LINK

PLUG IN	POWER UP	GO!

PLUG IN

You can solve one-step inequalities by using the inverse operation on both sides.

$$x + 5 > 8$$
$$x + 5 - 5 > 8 - 5$$
$$x > 3$$

POWER UP

You can write two-step inequalities to represent a word problem.

The cost of an airline ticket, $120 plus $15 per bag, must be no more than $200.

$$120 + 15b \le 200$$

I see! I can write and solve an inequality to solve a real-world problem.

WORK TOGETHER

You can use a Number Line to represent the solution set of a two-step inequality.

- Subtract 5 from both sides of the inequality.

- Divide both sides by 2.

- To graph, place a closed circle at 4 because 4 is a solution. Shade to the left of 4 because the solution set includes values less than 4.

- The number line represents the solution set for $2z + 5 \leq 13$.

Solve $2z + 5 \leq 13$.
Graph the solution set.

$2z + 5 - 5 \leq 13 - 5$

$2z \leq 8$

$\dfrac{2z}{2} \leq \dfrac{8}{2}$

$z \leq 4$

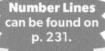

$$\xleftarrow{\hspace{2cm}}\begin{array}{ccccccccccc} & & & & & & & & & & \\ -5 & -4 & -3 & -2 & -1 & 0 & 1 & 2 & 3 & 4 & 5 \end{array}\xrightarrow{\hspace{1cm}}$$

I can use a number from the shaded part of the number line in the original inequality to check my work.

Number Lines can be found on p. 231.

A Write an inequality to represent the problem. Then solve and graph the solution.

DO

Jake bakes cakes for a fund-raiser. He spent $50 on supplies and sells each cake for $25. He wants to make more than $100 for the fund-raiser, as well as pay for the supplies. What is the number of cakes, c, Jake needs to sell to reach his goal?

❶ Write the inequality.

❷ Use inverse operations to solve. Add, then divide.

❸ Graph the solution.

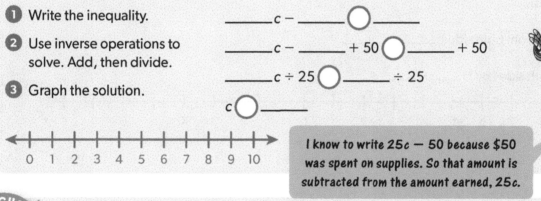

I know to write $25c - 50$ because $50 was spent on supplies. So that amount is subtracted from the amount earned, $25c$.

DISCUSS

How would you know whether to add 50 to both sides of an inequality first rather than divide both sides by 25?

PRACTICE

Solve the inequality and graph the solution set.

1 $4y - 17 > 7$

HINT
Undo the second operation first. Then undo the remaining operation.

Number Lines can be found on p. 233.

Add 17 to both sides: ___$4y > 24$___

Divide both sides by 4: _____

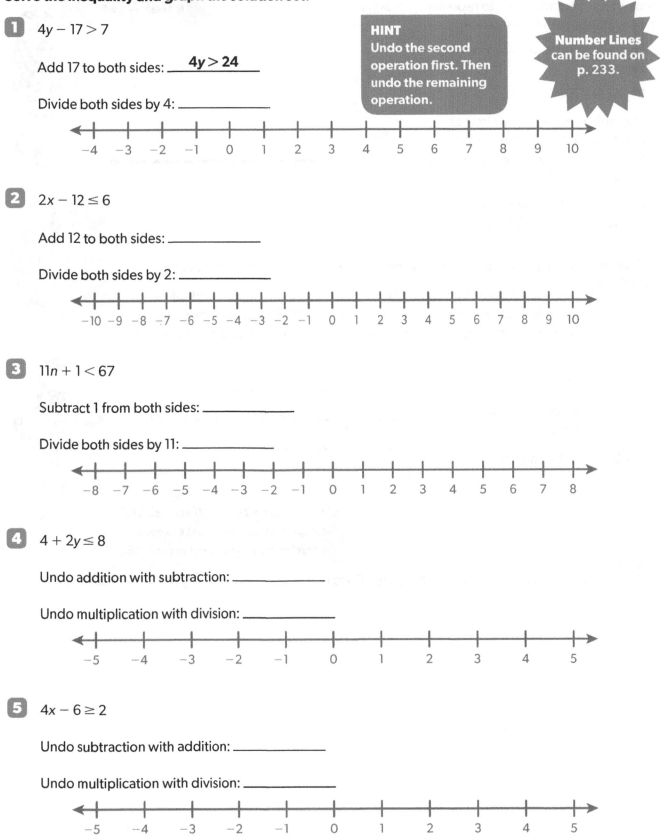

2 $2x - 12 \leq 6$

Add 12 to both sides: _____

Divide both sides by 2: _____

3 $11n + 1 < 67$

Subtract 1 from both sides: _____

Divide both sides by 11: _____

4 $4 + 2y \leq 8$

Undo addition with subtraction: _____

Undo multiplication with division: _____

5 $4x - 6 \geq 2$

Undo subtraction with addition: _____

Undo multiplication with division: _____

Write an inequality and tell whether the graph will have an open or closed circle.

6 Sean has $57 in his change jar and adds $3 each week. In how many weeks will the change jar have more than $72?

_____

7 Rea wants to buy a $64 watch. She has $15 and she makes $7 an hour. At least how many hours, h, would she have to work today to buy the watch?

_____

8 Elijah needs at least $2,150 to buy a used car. He already has $1,800 saved in his bank account. If Elijah saves an additional $35 a week, in how many weeks will he have saved enough to buy his car?

_____

Solve.

9 A cell phone plan charges $90 a month, plus $2 per hour of Web access. With how many hours of Web access will the monthly bill be under $100?

_____

> **REMEMBER**
> Try values in your solution set in the inequality to make sure your answer makes sense!

10 Delilah gets paid $15 an hour to work at a deli. She also makes $25 a week in tips. What is the number of hours she will have to work in one week to buy a tablet that costs at least $175?

_____

Correct the Error

Marina tries to solve the following inequality for x.

$$4x + 22 \leq 42$$
$$4x \leq 64$$
$$x \leq 256$$

What can you tell Marina about her work?

> Marina would have discovered her mistake if she had tried values from her incorrect solution set in the original inequality.

PROBLEM SOLVING

WALK-A-THON

READ

Isa collects donations for a charity walk. One group of sponsors will donate a total of $20 for each mile she walks. Another group of sponsors will donate $400 no matter how far she walks. What number of miles should Isa walk if she wants to raise at least $1,000?

PLAN

• What is the problem asking you to find?

the number of _____ Isa should walk

• What do you need to know to solve this problem?

One group will donate __$20__ per mile she walks.

One group will donate _____ no matter how far she walks.

Isa wants to raise at least _____.

SOLVE

Write an inequality to represent the situation. Let m represent the number of miles Isa walks.

_____ m + _____ $\geq$ _____

Find the solution set.

$m \geq$ _____

CHECK

Substitute a value from the solution set in the original inequality.

The solution set is any value greater than or equal to _____.

Select a value from the solution set. $m =$ _____

Substitute the value into the inequality. $20 \times$ _____ $+ 400 \geq 1{,}000$

_____ $+ 400 \geq 1{,}000$

The statement is true. _____ $\geq 1{,}000$

Isa must walk at least _____ miles in order to meet her goal.

> I could have picked any value in the solution set to check my work.

PRACTICE

Use the problem-solving steps to help you.

1 Pierre can spend no more than $49 on lunch for the art club. If sandwiches cost $3 each and Pierre spends a total of $13 on drinks, how many sandwiches can he buy?

CHECKLIST
- [ ] READ
- [ ] PLAN
- [ ] SOLVE
- [ ] CHECK

2 A farmer can spend up to $30,000 on farm equipment. He buys a tractor for $7,500. He also needs to buy storage bins that cost $2,500 each. How many storage bins can the farmer buy?

CHECKLIST
- [ ] READ
- [ ] PLAN
- [ ] SOLVE
- [ ] CHECK

3 Marcy must score an average of at least 90% between her two exams to make the math honor roll. If she scores a 94% on one of the exams, what score can she get on the other exam to make the math honor roll?

CHECKLIST
- [ ] READ
- [ ] PLAN
- [ ] SOLVE
- [ ] CHECK

PLUG IN | Writing and Solving Proportions

A pet store has 3 dogs for every 5 cats. If the ratio is constant, how many dogs are there when there are 20 cats in the pet store?

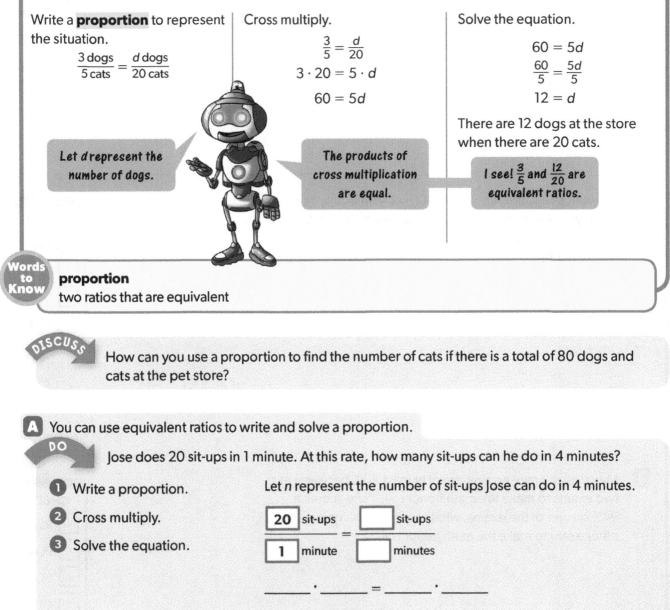

Write a **proportion** to represent the situation.

$$\frac{3 \text{ dogs}}{5 \text{ cats}} = \frac{d \text{ dogs}}{20 \text{ cats}}$$

Cross multiply.

$$\frac{3}{5} = \frac{d}{20}$$
$$3 \cdot 20 = 5 \cdot d$$
$$60 = 5d$$

Solve the equation.

$$60 = 5d$$
$$\frac{60}{5} = \frac{5d}{5}$$
$$12 = d$$

There are 12 dogs at the store when there are 20 cats.

Let *d* represent the number of dogs.

The products of cross multiplication are equal.

I see! $\frac{3}{5}$ and $\frac{12}{20}$ are equivalent ratios.

Words to Know

proportion
two ratios that are equivalent

DISCUSS

How can you use a proportion to find the number of cats if there is a total of 80 dogs and cats at the pet store?

A You can use equivalent ratios to write and solve a proportion.

DO

Jose does 20 sit-ups in 1 minute. At this rate, how many sit-ups can he do in 4 minutes?

① Write a proportion.

② Cross multiply.

③ Solve the equation.

Let *n* represent the number of sit-ups Jose can do in 4 minutes.

$$\frac{\boxed{20} \text{ sit-ups}}{\boxed{1} \text{ minute}} = \frac{\boxed{} \text{ sit-ups}}{\boxed{} \text{ minutes}}$$

$$\underline{} \cdot \underline{} = \underline{} \cdot \underline{}$$

$$\underline{} = \underline{}$$

Jose can do _____ sit-ups in 4 minutes.

B You can use a proportion to write and solve an equation.

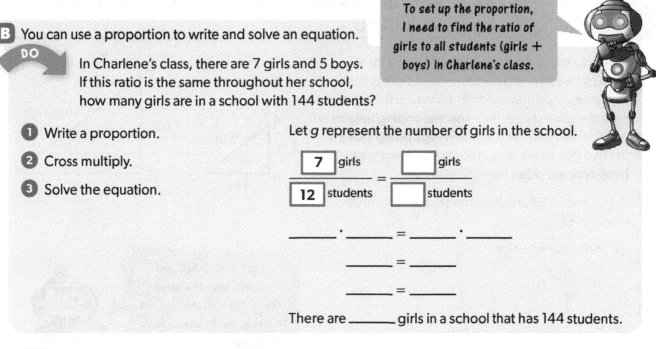

To set up the proportion, I need to find the ratio of girls to all students (girls + boys) in Charlene's class.

DO

In Charlene's class, there are 7 girls and 5 boys. If this ratio is the same throughout her school, how many girls are in a school with 144 students?

1 Write a proportion.

2 Cross multiply.

3 Solve the equation.

Let g represent the number of girls in the school.

$$\frac{\boxed{7} \text{ girls}}{\boxed{12} \text{ students}} = \frac{\boxed{} \text{ girls}}{\boxed{} \text{ students}}$$

_____ · _____ = _____ · _____

_____ = _____

_____ = _____

There are _____ girls in a school that has 144 students.

DISCUSS

What are two different ways you could find the number of boys in Charlene's school by using your answer to the above problem?

PRACTICE

Solve the proportion for the variable.

1 $\frac{6}{8} = \frac{x}{12}$

_____6___ · ___12___ = ___8___ · ___x___

_____ = _____

_____ = _____

2 $\frac{p}{2} = \frac{6}{3}$

___p___ · ___3___ = _____ · _____

_____ = _____

_____ = _____

Write a proportion to solve the problem.

3 How much will 6 pencils cost if 3 pencils cost 75¢?

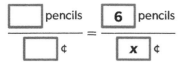

$$\frac{\boxed{} \text{ pencils}}{\boxed{} ¢} = \frac{\boxed{6} \text{ pencils}}{\boxed{x} ¢}$$

_____

4 Maria earned $42 for 6 hours of work. How much will she get for 15 hours of work?

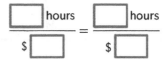

$$\frac{\boxed{} \text{ hours}}{\$\boxed{}} = \frac{\boxed{} \text{ hours}}{\$\boxed{}}$$

_____

The POWER UP box with the title.

POWER UP · Using Proportions to Find Lengths of Sides

Think of a small square and a large square, or a small circle and a large circle — these figures have the same shape, but are different in size. If two figures have the same shape, their **corresponding angles** are equal in measure. Also, the **corresponding sides** of the two figures are proportional. The lengths of **proportional sides** form equal ratios.

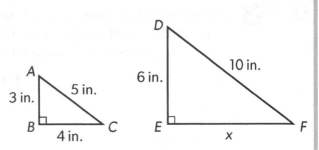

$\triangle ABC$ and $\triangle DEF$ are the same shape. What is the length of $\overline{EF}$?

1. Write a proportion.

$$\frac{AB}{DE} = \frac{BC}{EF}$$

$$\frac{3}{6} = \frac{4}{x}$$

2. Cross multiply to solve for x.

$$3 \cdot x = 6 \cdot 4$$

$$3x = 24$$

$$\frac{3x}{3} = \frac{24}{3}$$

$$x = 8$$

The length of $\overline{EF}$ is 8 inches.

> I get it! If $\triangle ABC$ and $\triangle DEF$ have the same shape, then I know that the corresponding angles have the same measure and that the corresponding sides are proportional!

Words to Know

corresponding angles	corresponding sides	proportional sides
angles of two figures that are in the same relative positions	sides of two figures that are in the same relative positions	corresponding sides with lengths that form equal ratios
$\angle M$ and $\angle X$	MN and XY	$\frac{MN}{XY} = \frac{NO}{YZ} = \frac{OM}{ZX}$
$\angle N$ and $\angle Y$	NO and YZ	
$\angle O$ and $\angle Z$	OM and ZX	

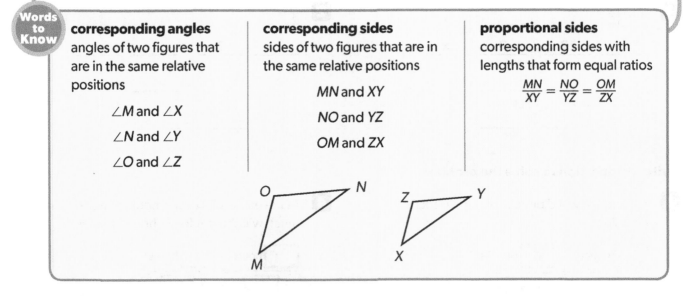

DISCUSS
How can you show that the three pairs of corresponding sides of two triangles are proportional sides?

A You can use proportions to find missing side lengths.

DO

Rectangles *ABCD* and *EFGH* have the same shape. What is the length of $\overline{FG}$?

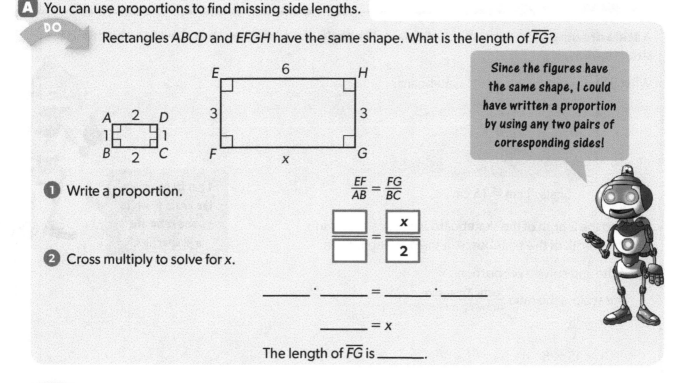

> Since the figures have the same shape, I could have written a proportion by using any two pairs of corresponding sides!

1 Write a proportion.

$$\frac{EF}{AB} = \frac{FG}{BC}$$

$$\frac{\boxed{}}{\boxed{}} = \frac{\boxed{x}}{\boxed{2}}$$

2 Cross multiply to solve for *x*.

$$\underline{\hspace{1cm}} \cdot \underline{\hspace{1cm}} = \underline{\hspace{1cm}} \cdot \underline{\hspace{1cm}}$$

$$\underline{\hspace{1cm}} = x$$

The length of $\overline{FG}$ is _____.

DISCUSS

Alyssa says that quadrilaterals *STUV* and *WXYZ* have the same shape. Is she correct? Explain.

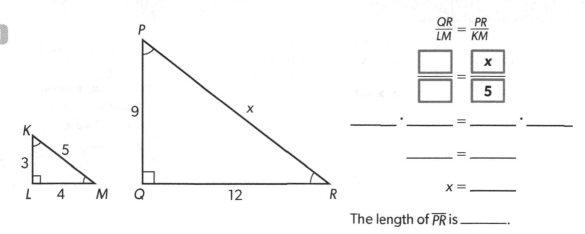

PRACTICE

The triangles have the same shape. Write and solve a proportion to find the unknown side length.

1

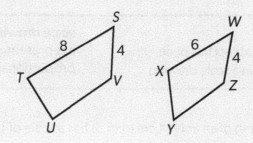

$$\frac{QR}{LM} = \frac{PR}{KM}$$

$$\frac{\boxed{}}{\boxed{}} = \frac{\boxed{x}}{\boxed{5}}$$

$$\underline{\hspace{1cm}} \cdot \underline{\hspace{1cm}} = \underline{\hspace{1cm}} \cdot \underline{\hspace{1cm}}$$

$$\underline{\hspace{1cm}} = \underline{\hspace{1cm}}$$

$$x = \underline{\hspace{1cm}}$$

The length of $\overline{PR}$ is _____.

A **scale drawing** represents an actual object. The **scale** compares the actual size of an object and the size of its drawing.

What is the length of the actual skateboard?

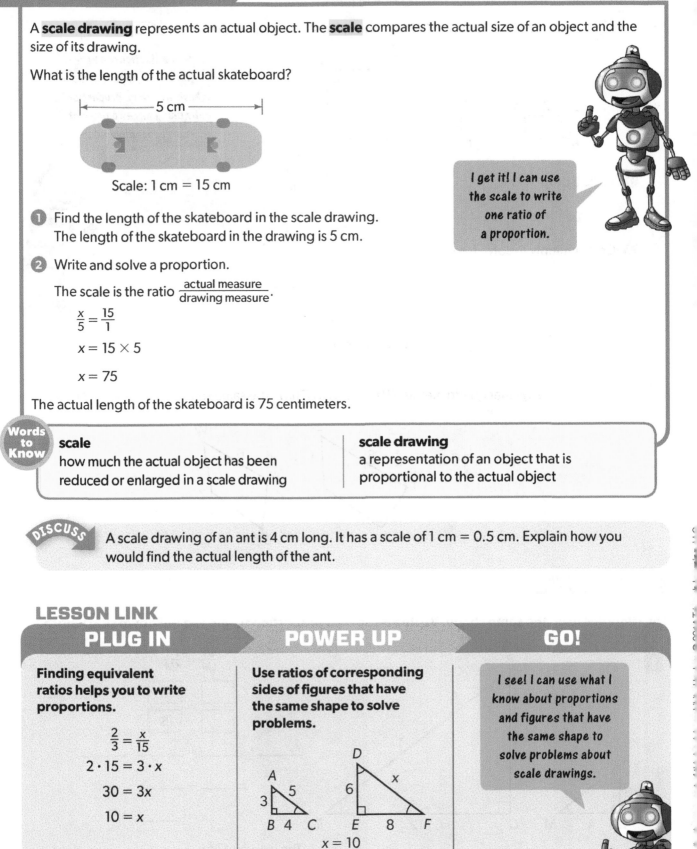

Scale: 1 cm = 15 cm

I get it! I can use the scale to write one ratio of a proportion.

1. Find the length of the skateboard in the scale drawing.
   The length of the skateboard in the drawing is 5 cm.

2. Write and solve a proportion.
   The scale is the ratio $\frac{\text{actual measure}}{\text{drawing measure}}$.

   $$\frac{x}{5} = \frac{15}{1}$$

   $$x = 15 \times 5$$

   $$x = 75$$

The actual length of the skateboard is 75 centimeters.

Words to Know

scale
how much the actual object has been reduced or enlarged in a scale drawing

scale drawing
a representation of an object that is proportional to the actual object

DISCUSS A scale drawing of an ant is 4 cm long. It has a scale of 1 cm = 0.5 cm. Explain how you would find the actual length of the ant.

LESSON LINK

PLUG IN	POWER UP	GO!
Finding equivalent ratios helps you to write proportions. $$\frac{2}{3} = \frac{x}{15}$$ $$2 \cdot 15 = 3 \cdot x$$ $$30 = 3x$$ $$10 = x$$	Use ratios of corresponding sides of figures that have the same shape to solve problems. $x = 10$	*I see! I can use what I know about proportions and figures that have the same shape to solve problems about scale drawings.*

WORK TOGETHER

You can sketch a scale drawing by finding the proportions of corresponding sides of figures that have the same shape.

- Write proportions to find the length and width of the scale drawing.

- The sketch shows the scale drawing of the room.

The actual dimensions of a room are 40 feet by 20 feet. Sketch a scale drawing of the room with a scale of 1 cm = 4 feet.

Scale drawing length:

$$\frac{1\,cm}{4\,ft} = \frac{l}{40}$$

$$1 \cdot 40 = 4 \cdot l$$

$$40 = 4l$$

$$10 = l$$

Scale drawing width:

$$\frac{1\,cm}{4\,ft} = \frac{w}{20}$$

$$1 \cdot 20 = 4 \cdot w$$

$$20 = 4w$$

$$5 = w$$

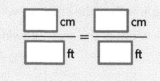

I get it! I use the scale and the actual length and width to find the length and width of a scale drawing.

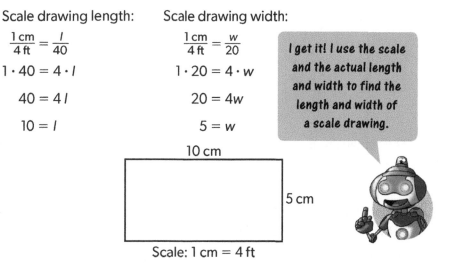

10 cm

5 cm

Scale: 1 cm = 4 ft

A You can find the actual measures of an object from a scale drawing.

DO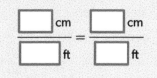

Christopher makes a scale drawing of his favorite car. The car is 15 cm long and 8 cm high. If the scale is 1 cm = 0.75 ft, what are the measurements of the actual car?

1 List the measures of the length and height of the scale drawing.

Length of scale drawing: _____

Height of scale drawing: _____

2 Write proportions to find the actual length and height of the car.

Length of actual car:

$$\frac{\boxed{}\,cm}{\boxed{}\,ft} = \frac{\boxed{}\,cm}{\boxed{}\,ft}$$

_____ · _____ = _____ · _____

_____ = _____

Height of actual car:

$$\frac{\boxed{}\,cm}{\boxed{}\,ft} = \frac{\boxed{}\,cm}{\boxed{}\,ft}$$

_____ · _____ = _____ · _____

_____ = _____

The length of the actual car is _____ ft.

The height of the actual car is _____ ft.

DISCUSS

Suppose the scale for the scale drawing is 1 cm = 1 ft. Without computing, what are the length and width of the actual car?

PRACTICE

Write and solve a proportion to find the length of the actual object.

1 Scale: 1 in. = 3 ft

Length on a scale drawing: 6 in.

$$\frac{\boxed{}\text{ in.}}{\boxed{}\text{ ft}} = \frac{\boxed{}\text{ in.}}{\boxed{}\text{ ft}}$$

The actual length is _____ feet.

2 Scale: 5 cm = 15 km

Length on a scale drawing: 7 cm

$$\frac{\boxed{}\text{ cm}}{\boxed{}\text{ km}} = \frac{\boxed{}\text{ cm}}{\boxed{}\text{ km}}$$

The actual length is _____ kilometers.

3 A room has a length of 35 feet and a width of 25 feet. Make a scale drawing of the room with the scale 1 cm = 5 ft.

> **REMEMBER**
> Write a proportion using the ratios of scale measure to actual measure.

Length of scale drawing:

$$\frac{\boxed{1}\text{ cm}}{\boxed{5}\text{ ft}} = \frac{\boxed{l}\text{ cm}}{\boxed{}\text{ ft}}$$

Solve for l.

Width of scale drawing:

$$\frac{\boxed{}\text{ cm}}{\boxed{}\text{ ft}} = \frac{\boxed{}\text{ cm}}{\boxed{}\text{ ft}}$$

Solve for w.

The length of the scale drawing is _____ centimeters.

The width of the scale drawing is _____ centimeters.

Solve.

4 A road is 9 inches long on a road map. If the scale on the map is 1 inch = 6 miles, what is the actual length of the road?

_____ miles

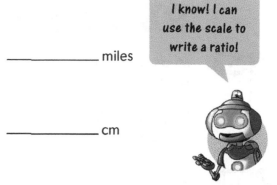

5 The scale drawing shows a logo design for a scoreboard. What will be the perimeter of the actual logo? Use a ruler to measure the drawing.

_____ cm

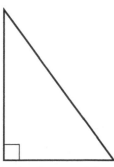

Scale: 1 cm = 20 cm

6 The scale drawing shows a rectangular garden. Mike plans to build a fence around it. How many feet of fencing does he need to go around the garden? Use a ruler to measure the drawing.

_____ feet

Scale: 1 in. = 10 ft

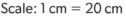

DISCUSS

Writing a proportion can help me to understand a problem with scale drawings better.

Make Sense of Problems

Sarah and Matt both make scale drawings of the classroom. Sarah makes the scale of her drawing 2 cm = 1 ft. Matt makes the scale of his drawing 3 cm = 1.5 ft. How will the sizes of their scale drawings compare? Explain.

PROBLEM SOLVING

READING MAPS

READ
Megan is planning to drive from Dallas to Austin, and then to Houston. Finally, she will drive back home to Dallas. Use a ruler to find the distance between the cities on the map. Then use the scale to find the total actual distance of her road trip.

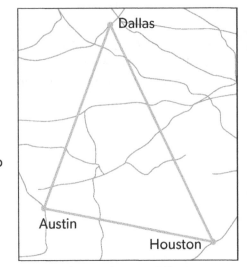

Scale: 2 cm = 75 mi

PLAN
• What is the problem asking you to find?

the total _____ distance of Megan's road trip

• What do you need to know?

The scale is _____ = _____.

Measure the distances between cities to the nearest tenth of a centimeter.

• How can you solve the problem?

You can set up and solve proportions to find actual distances.

SOLVE
Complete the table. Use a proportion to find each actual distance. Round the actual distance to the nearest whole number.

City	Map Distance	Actual Distance
Dallas to Austin	**5.2 cm**	
Austin to Houston		
Houston to Dallas		
Total Distance		

> I get it! A map is a scale drawing.

CHECK
Write and solve a proportion for the total distance on the map.

$$\frac{\boxed{}\ \text{cm}}{\boxed{}\ \text{mi}} = \frac{\boxed{}\ \text{cm}}{\boxed{}\ \text{mi}}$$

$x =$ _____ miles

The total actual distance is about _____.

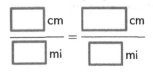

PRACTICE

Use the problem-solving steps to help you. Use a ruler when needed.

1 Dylan plans to make a large triangular flag to support his favorite sports team. What are the side lengths of the actual flag?

Scale: 1 cm = 1.5 m

CHECKLIST
- [ ] READ
- [ ] PLAN
- [ ] SOLVE
- [ ] CHECK

2 The scale drawing shows a square poster that Kayla designed. What is the perimeter of the poster?

Scale: 1 cm = 1 ft

CHECKLIST
- [ ] READ
- [ ] PLAN
- [ ] SOLVE
- [ ] CHECK

I remember! The perimeter of a figure is the sum of its side lengths.

3 Hector wants to enclose a pen for his two dogs with a fence. How many feet of fencing will he need for his pen?

Scale: $\frac{1}{2}$ in. = 5 ft

CHECKLIST
- [ ] READ
- [ ] PLAN
- [ ] SOLVE
- [ ] CHECK

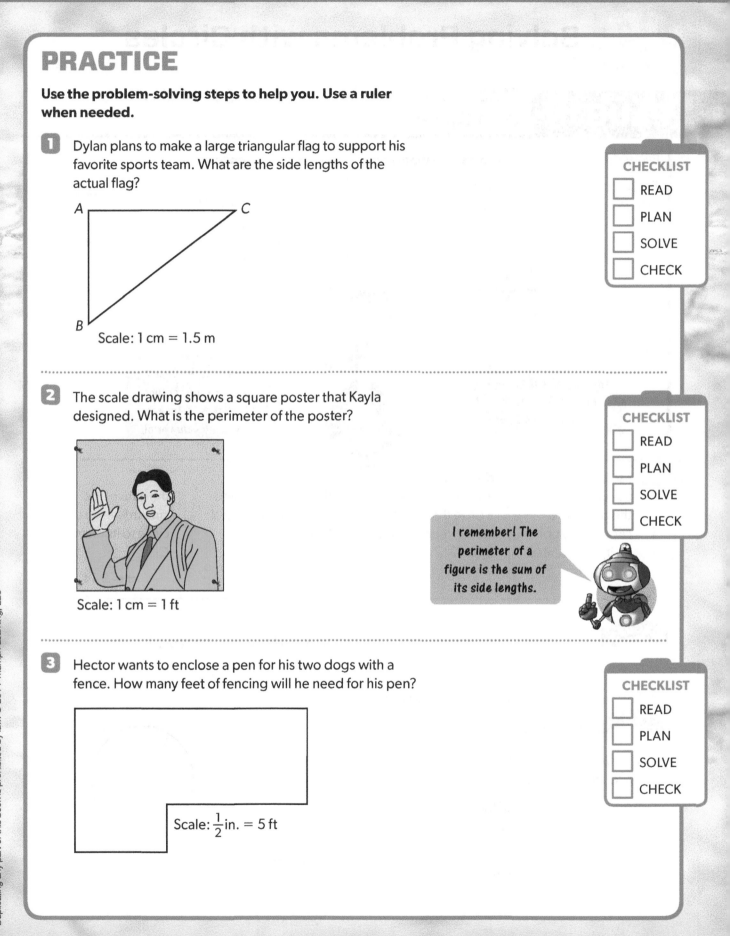

Solving Problems with Circles

PLUG IN Radius, Diameter, and Circumference of a Circle

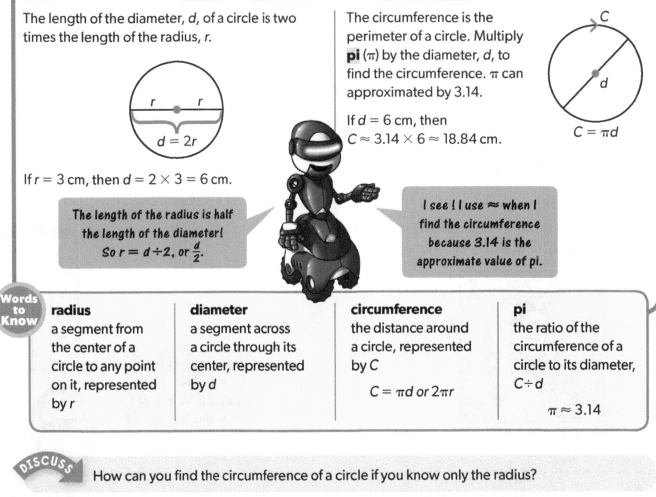

Every circle has a center, a **radius** (*r*), a **diameter** (*d*), and a **circumference** (*C*).

The length of the diameter, *d*, of a circle is two times the length of the radius, *r*.

$d = 2r$

If *r* = 3 cm, then *d* = 2 × 3 = 6 cm.

The circumference is the perimeter of a circle. Multiply **pi** (π) by the diameter, *d*, to find the circumference. π can approximated by 3.14.

If *d* = 6 cm, then
$C ≈ 3.14 × 6 ≈ 18.84$ cm.

$C = πd$

The length of the radius is half the length of the diameter!
So $r = d ÷ 2$, or $\frac{d}{2}$.

I see! I use ≈ when I find the circumference because 3.14 is the approximate value of pi.

Words to Know

radius	**diameter**	**circumference**	**pi**
a segment from the center of a circle to any point on it, represented by *r*	a segment across a circle through its center, represented by *d*	the distance around a circle, represented by *C* $C = πd$ or $2πr$	the ratio of the circumference of a circle to its diameter, $C ÷ d$ $π ≈ 3.14$

DISCUSS How can you find the circumference of a circle if you know only the radius?

A You can use multiplication to find the diameter of a circle.

DO Find the diameter of the circle.

r = 2 cm

1 Write the formula for the diameter of a circle.

$d = \underline{\quad 2r \quad}$

2 Plug in the length of the radius in the formula and multiply.

$d = \underline{\quad\quad} × \underline{\quad\quad} = \underline{\quad\quad}$ cm

3 Write the length of the diameter.

The diameter measures _____ cm.

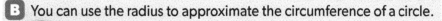

B You can use the radius to approximate the circumference of a circle.

DO   Find the circumference of the circle.

r = 4.5 m

1. Write the formula for the circumference using the diameter.

   $C =$ ___**πd**___

   The length of the diameter is _____ times the length of the radius.

2. Describe the relationship between diameter and radius.

   $d =$ _____

   $C =$ ___**πd**___ or _____

3. Write a circumference formula using *r*.

   $C \approx$ _____ × _____ × _____

   $C \approx$ _____ × _____

4. Plug in 3.14 for π and the length of the radius in the circumference formula.

   $C \approx$ _____ m

   The circumference is approximately

5. Multiply. Write the approximate circumference.

   _____ meters.

> I remember! The ≈ symbol means "is approximately equal to."

Circle Formulas can be found on p. 247.

DISCUSS   Rose measures the radius of her bicycle wheel to be 14 inches. She orders a new tire for the wheel by finding its circumference. However, she calculates its value using 3 for π instead of 3.14. What should she expect when her tire arrives?

PRACTICE

Find the length of the radius or diameter when given the other measure.

1. If $d = 8$, then $r =$ _____.

2. If $r = 15$, then $d =$ _____.

Find the circumference of the circle. Use 3.14 for π. Show your work.

3.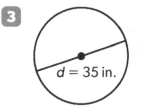
   d = 35 in.

4.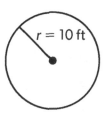
   r = 10 ft

5.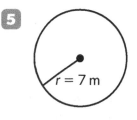
   r = 7 m

_____   _____   _____

Area of a Circle

The circumference of a circle is related to the **area of a circle**.

This octagon is divided into 8 equivalent triangles. Its shape is close to, but not exactly, a circle.

If cut apart, the 8 triangles can be arranged as a parallelogram. If half of the first triangle is cut off and moved to the end, the parallelogram becomes a rectangle.

The bases of four triangles, or about half the circumference of the circle, make up the length of the rectangle. We can approximate the length: $l \approx \frac{1}{2}(2\pi r) = \pi r$.

The width of the rectangle is equal to the height, h, of the triangle. The height, h, is about the same as the radius, r, of the circle, so we can approximate the width: $w \approx r$.

The formula for the area of a rectangle is $A = lw$. If we substitute πr for l and r for w, the result is the formula for the area of a circle.

$A = \pi r \times r$, or πr^2.

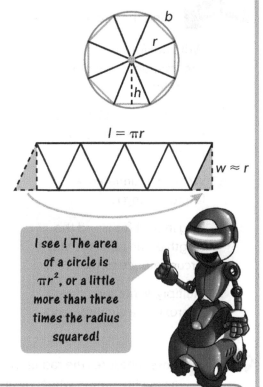

I see ! The area of a circle is πr^2, or a little more than three times the radius squared!

Words to Know

area of a circle
the total number of square units that fit inside the circle; The formula for the area of a circle is $A = \pi r^2$.

DISCUSS

Juanita calculates the circumference and area for a circle with radius 2 cm. She finds they are both equal to 4π. She asks how the distance around a circle can be the same as the area inside a circle. What would you tell her?

A You can use the radius to approximate the area of a circle.

DO Find the area of the circle.

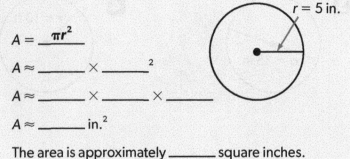

1. Write the formula for the area of a circle.

2. Plug in 3.14 for π and the length of the radius in the formula.

3. Multiply. Write the approximate area.

$A = \underline{\pi r^2}$

$A \approx \underline{\hspace{1cm}} \times \underline{\hspace{1cm}}^2$

$A \approx \underline{\hspace{1cm}} \times \underline{\hspace{1cm}} \times \underline{\hspace{1cm}}$

$A \approx \underline{\hspace{1cm}}$ in.^{2}

The area is approximately $\underline{\hspace{1cm}}$ square inches.

$r = 5$ in.

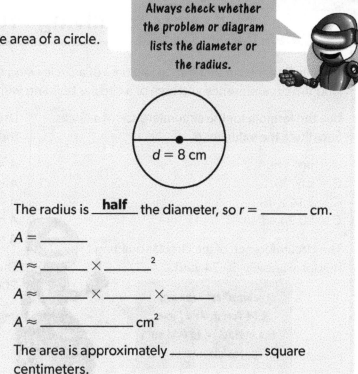

Always check whether the problem or diagram lists the diameter or the radius.

B You can use diameter to find the approximate area of a circle.

DO Find the area of the circle.

1 Find the radius of the circle.

2 Write the formula for the area of the circle.

3 Plug in 3.14 for π and the length of the radius in the formula.

4 Multiply. Write the approximate area.

$d = 8$ cm

The radius is __**half**__ the diameter, so $r = $ _____ cm.

$A = $ _____

$A \approx $ _____ $\times$ _____^{2}

$A \approx $ _____ $\times$ _____ $\times$ _____

$A \approx $ _____ cm^2

The area is approximately _____ square centimeters.

DISCUSS Rob made an error when he solved for the area of the circle shown. What can you tell him about his work? What is the correct answer?

$A = \pi \times 3^2$

$A \approx 3.14 \times 6$

$A \approx 18.84$ cm^2

$d = 6$ cm

Circle Formulas can be found on p. 247.

PRACTICE

Find the approximate area of the circle. Use 3.14 for π. Show your work.

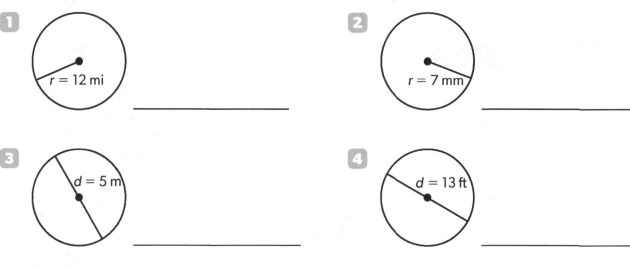

1 $r = 12$ mi

_____

2 $r = 7$ mm

_____

3 $d = 5$ m

_____

4 $d = 13$ ft

_____

Solving Problems with Circles

You can find the circumference and area of a circle using formulas.
Find the circumference and area of a circular building with diameter of 16 yards.

Use the formula for the circumference of a circle. Substitute the value for *d*.

$C = \pi d$
$C = \pi \times 16$
$C \approx 3.14 \times 16$
$C \approx 50.24$ yd

The circumference of the circular building is approximately 50.24 yards.

> I remember! I can use 3.14 for π. And I use the symbol ≈ to find an approximate value.

Use the formula for the area of a circle. Substitute the value for *r*.

$A = \pi r^2$
$A \approx 3.14 \times 8^2$
$A \approx 3.14 \times 8 \times 8$
$A \approx 3.14 \times 64$
$A \approx 200.96$ yd^2

The area of the circular building is approximately 200.96 square yards.

> I have to first find the radius. Since the diameter is 16, the radius is 16 ÷ 2 = 8.

DISCUSS

Tina made an error when solving for the area of the circle shown. Identify her error, and write the correct answer. How far off was her answer?

$A = \pi 11^2$

$A \approx 3.14 \times 11 \times 11$

$A \approx 3.14 \times 121$

$A \approx 379.94$ mm^2

$d = 11$ mm

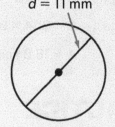

LESSON LINK

PLUG IN	POWER UP	GO!

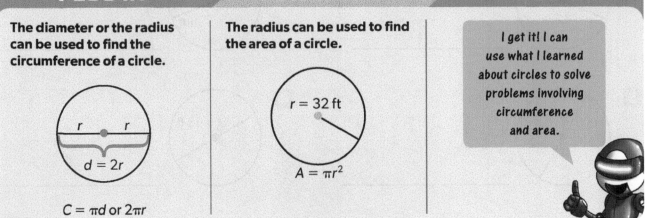

The diameter or the radius can be used to find the circumference of a circle.

r r
$d = 2r$

$C = \pi d$ or $2\pi r$

The radius can be used to find the area of a circle.

$r = 32$ ft

$A = \pi r^2$

> I get it! I can use what I learned about circles to solve problems involving circumference and area.

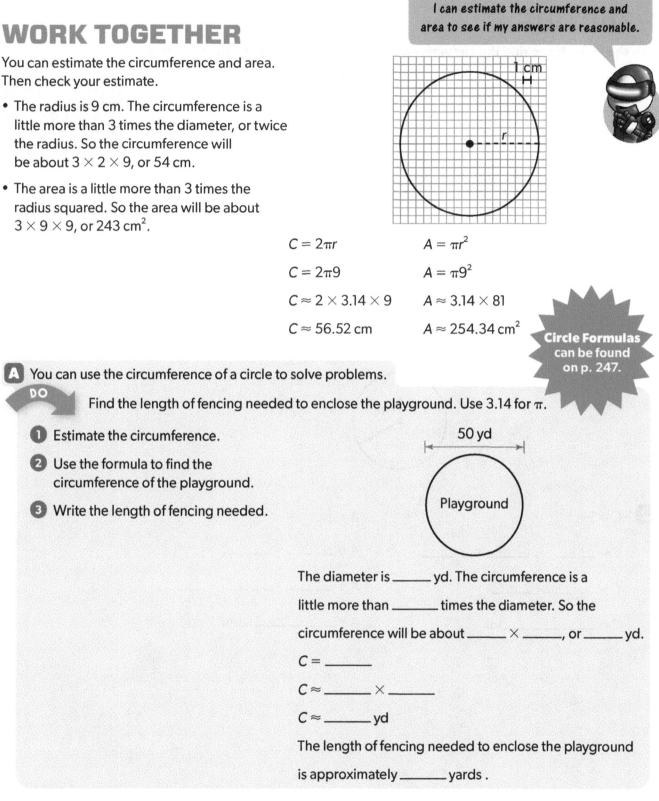

> I can estimate the circumference and area to see if my answers are reasonable.

WORK TOGETHER

You can estimate the circumference and area.
Then check your estimate.

- The radius is 9 cm. The circumference is a little more than 3 times the diameter, or twice the radius. So the circumference will be about $3 \times 2 \times 9$, or 54 cm.

- The area is a little more than 3 times the radius squared. So the area will be about $3 \times 9 \times 9$, or 243 cm².

$C = 2\pi r$	$A = \pi r^2$
$C = 2\pi 9$	$A = \pi 9^2$
$C \approx 2 \times 3.14 \times 9$	$A \approx 3.14 \times 81$
$C \approx 56.52$ cm	$A \approx 254.34$ cm²

> **Circle Formulas** can be found on p. 247.

A You can use the circumference of a circle to solve problems.

DO Find the length of fencing needed to enclose the playground. Use 3.14 for π.

1 Estimate the circumference.

2 Use the formula to find the circumference of the playground.

3 Write the length of fencing needed.

50 yd

Playground

The diameter is _____ yd. The circumference is a little more than _____ times the diameter. So the circumference will be about _____ × _____, or _____ yd.

$C =$ _____

$C \approx$ _____ × _____

$C \approx$ _____ yd

The length of fencing needed to enclose the playground is approximately _____ yards .

DISCUSS Look at the formulas for the circumference and area of a circle. How is the formula for circumference related to the formula for area?

PRACTICE

Use the formulas to find the circumference and area of the circle. Use 3.14 for π.

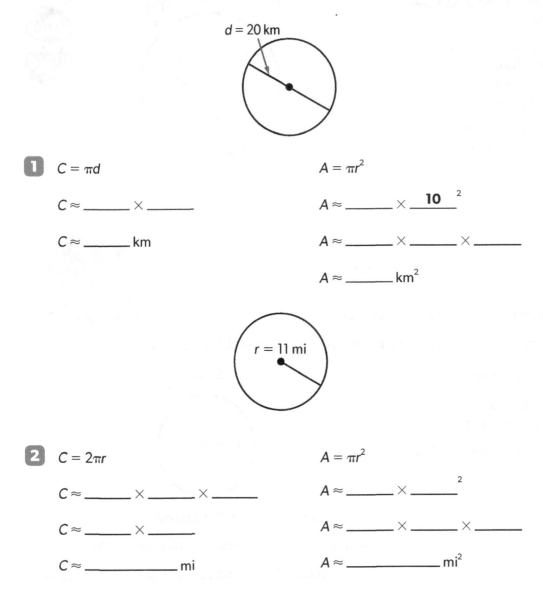

$d = 20$ km

1 $C = \pi d$

$C \approx$ _____ × _____

$C \approx$ _____ km

$A = \pi r^2$

$A \approx$ _____ × $\underline{\textbf{10}}^2$

$A \approx$ _____ × _____ × _____

$A \approx$ _____ km^2

$r = 11$ mi

2 $C = 2\pi r$

$C \approx$ _____ × _____ × _____

$C \approx$ _____ × _____

$C \approx$ _____ mi

$A = \pi r^2$

$A \approx$ _____ × _____^{2}

$A \approx$ _____ × _____ × _____

$A \approx$ _____ mi^2

Estimate first. Then solve. Use 3.14 for π.

3 Ali needs a pool cover for her circular pool. What is the circumference of the pool?

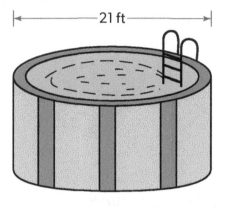

|←———— 21 ft ————→|

4 Tom is planning a circular flower garden for the yard. What area of the yard will be planted with flowers?

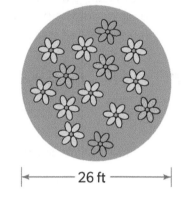

|←———— 26 ft ————→|

_____

Solve. Use 3.14 for π.

Sketch a diagram to make sure you understand what the problem is describing.

5 A sprinkler sprays water within a 5-meter radius as it spins in a circle. What is the approximate area of lawn that is watered by the sprinkler? _____

6 A hockey puck is 7.6 centimeters in diameter. What is the circumference of the puck? _____

DISCUSS

Make Sense of Problems

Kate keeps a circular photograph in a circular picture frame. The photograph has a diameter of 7 cm. The frame has a diameter of 15 cm. Describe the steps Kate can take to find the total distance around the outside and the inside of the picture frame.

What is the total distance around the outside and the inside of the picture frame?

Making a diagram can help you sort through the information given in a problem!

PROBLEM SOLVING

DUCKS AMUCK

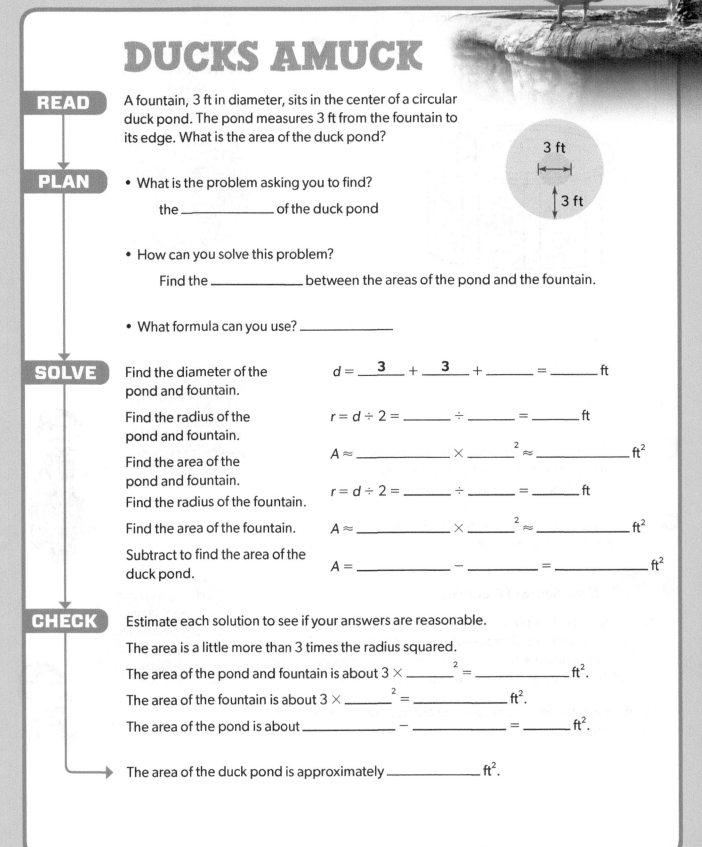

READ

A fountain, 3 ft in diameter, sits in the center of a circular duck pond. The pond measures 3 ft from the fountain to its edge. What is the area of the duck pond?

3 ft

|←——→|

3 ft

PLAN

• What is the problem asking you to find?

the _____ of the duck pond

• How can you solve this problem?

Find the _____ between the areas of the pond and the fountain.

• What formula can you use? _____

SOLVE

Find the diameter of the pond and fountain.

$d =$ **3** $+$ **3** $+$ _____ $=$ _____ ft

Find the radius of the pond and fountain.

$r = d \div 2 =$ _____ $\div$ _____ $=$ _____ ft

Find the area of the pond and fountain.

$A \approx$ _____ $\times$ _____$^2 \approx$ _____ ft^2

Find the radius of the fountain.

$r = d \div 2 =$ _____ $\div$ _____ $=$ _____ ft

Find the area of the fountain.

$A \approx$ _____ $\times$ _____$^2 \approx$ _____ ft^2

Subtract to find the area of the duck pond.

$A =$ _____ $-$ _____ $=$ _____ ft^2

CHECK

Estimate each solution to see if your answers are reasonable.

The area is a little more than 3 times the radius squared.

The area of the pond and fountain is about $3 \times$ _____$^2 =$ _____ ft^2.

The area of the fountain is about $3 \times$ _____$^2 =$ _____ ft^2.

The area of the pond is about _____ $-$ _____ $=$ _____ ft^2.

The area of the duck pond is approximately _____ ft^2.

PRACTICE

Use the problem-solving steps to help you. Use 3.14 for π.

Be sure to include the units in your answer!

1 Brad is replacing the topsoil in the community garden. If the area he is replacing is in the shape of a half circle with a diameter of 30 dm, how many square decimeters of the garden will he replace?

CHECKLIST
- [ ] READ
- [ ] PLAN
- [ ] SOLVE
- [ ] CHECK

2 The diameter of a basketball hoop is 18 inches. What is the largest circumference of a basketball that will fit through the hoop? Show your work.

CHECKLIST
- [ ] READ
- [ ] PLAN
- [ ] SOLVE
- [ ] CHECK

3 A circular window frame has a diameter of 22 inches. The glass window inside the frame has a radius of 10 inches. What is the area of the window frame not including the glass?

CHECKLIST
- [ ] READ
- [ ] PLAN
- [ ] SOLVE
- [ ] CHECK

PLUG IN Area of Triangles and Parallelograms

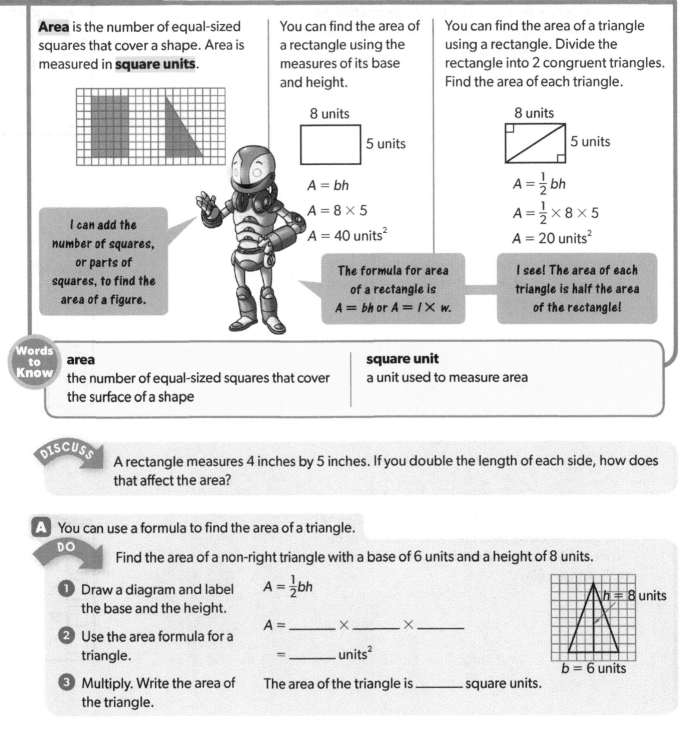

Area is the number of equal-sized squares that cover a shape. Area is measured in **square units**.

I can add the number of squares, or parts of squares, to find the area of a figure.

You can find the area of a rectangle using the measures of its base and height.

8 units

5 units

$A = bh$

$A = 8 \times 5$

$A = 40$ units^2

The formula for area of a rectangle is $A = bh$ or $A = l \times w$.

You can find the area of a triangle using a rectangle. Divide the rectangle into 2 congruent triangles. Find the area of each triangle.

8 units

5 units

$A = \frac{1}{2} bh$

$A = \frac{1}{2} \times 8 \times 5$

$A = 20$ units^2

I see! The area of each triangle is half the area of the rectangle!

Words to Know

area
the number of equal-sized squares that cover the surface of a shape

square unit
a unit used to measure area

DISCUSS A rectangle measures 4 inches by 5 inches. If you double the length of each side, how does that affect the area?

A You can use a formula to find the area of a triangle.

DO Find the area of a non-right triangle with a base of 6 units and a height of 8 units.

① Draw a diagram and label the base and the height.

② Use the area formula for a triangle.

③ Multiply. Write the area of the triangle.

$A = \frac{1}{2}bh$

$A = \underline{\hspace{1cm}} \times \underline{\hspace{1cm}} \times \underline{\hspace{1cm}}$

$= \underline{\hspace{1cm}}$ units^2

The area of the triangle is $\underline{\hspace{1cm}}$ square units.

$h = 8$ units

$b = 6$ units

B Use a diagram to find the area of a parallelogram.

> I see that a parallelogram has four sides. That means it's a quadrilateral, like a rectangle or a trapezoid.

DO Find the area of a parallelogram with a base of 9 cm and a height of 6 cm.

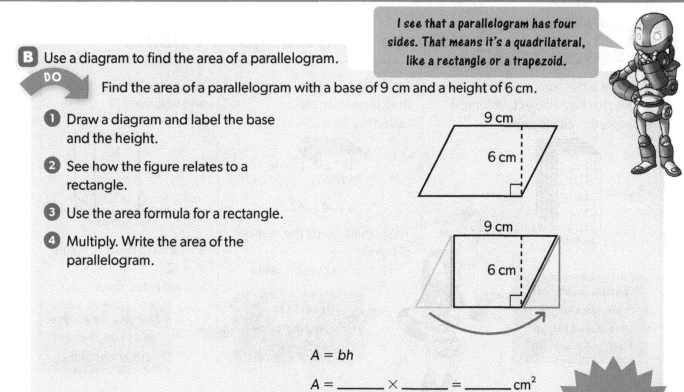

1. Draw a diagram and label the base and the height.

2. See how the figure relates to a rectangle.

3. Use the area formula for a rectangle.

4. Multiply. Write the area of the parallelogram.

$A = bh$

$A = \underline{\qquad} \times \underline{\qquad} = \underline{\qquad} \text{ cm}^2$

The area of the parallelogram is _____ square centimeters.

> Formulas for Area, A, can be found on p. 249.

PRACTICE

Find the area.

1

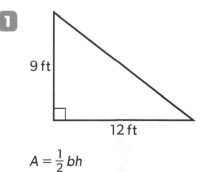

9 ft

12 ft

$A = \frac{1}{2} bh$

_____

2

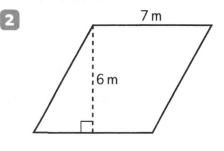

7 m

6 m

$A = bh$

_____

Volume of Rectangular Prisms

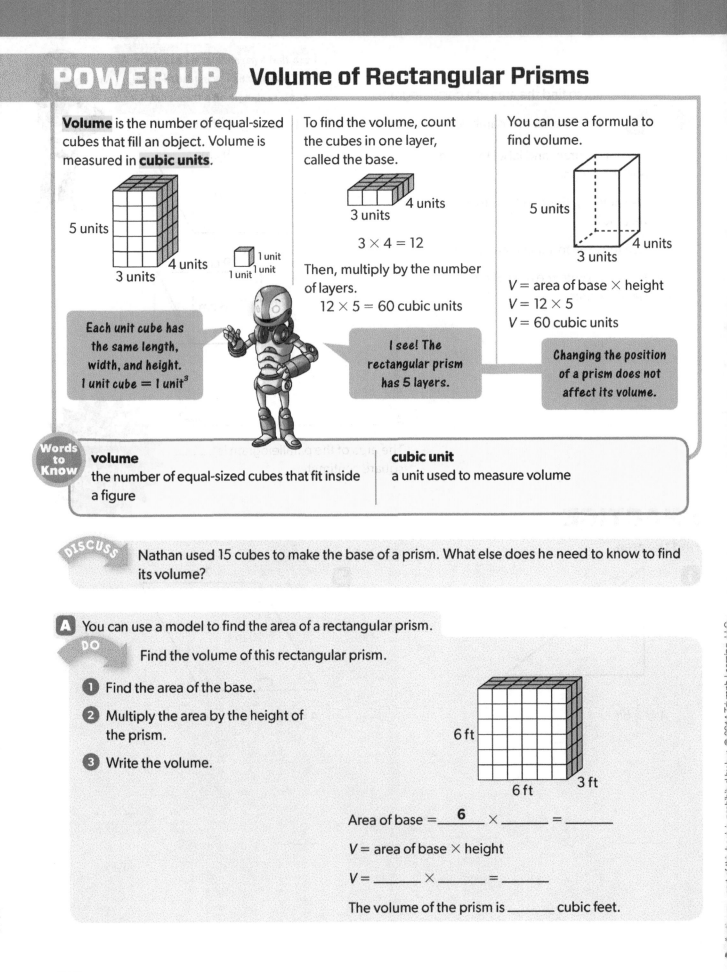

Volume is the number of equal-sized cubes that fill an object. Volume is measured in **cubic units**.

5 units
3 units
4 units

1 unit
1 unit 1 unit

Each unit cube has the same length, width, and height.
1 unit cube = 1 unit³

To find the volume, count the cubes in one layer, called the base.

4 units
3 units

$3 \times 4 = 12$

Then, multiply by the number of layers.

$12 \times 5 = 60$ cubic units

I see! The rectangular prism has 5 layers.

You can use a formula to find volume.

5 units
3 units
4 units

$V = $ area of base $\times$ height
$V = 12 \times 5$
$V = 60$ cubic units

Changing the position of a prism does not affect its volume.

Words to Know

volume
the number of equal-sized cubes that fit inside a figure

cubic unit
a unit used to measure volume

DISCUSS Nathan used 15 cubes to make the base of a prism. What else does he need to know to find its volume?

A You can use a model to find the area of a rectangular prism.

DO Find the volume of this rectangular prism.

1 Find the area of the base.

2 Multiply the area by the height of the prism.

3 Write the volume.

6 ft
6 ft
3 ft

Area of base = ___**6**___ × _____ = _____

$V = $ area of base $\times$ height

$V = $ _____ × _____ = _____

The volume of the prism is _____ cubic feet.

I remember! Prisms have the same volume no matter how they are turned.

B You can use a formula to find the volume of rectangular prisms.

DO Find the volume of rectangular prisms with the same dimensions.

1 Find the volume of each prism.

2 Compare the volumes.

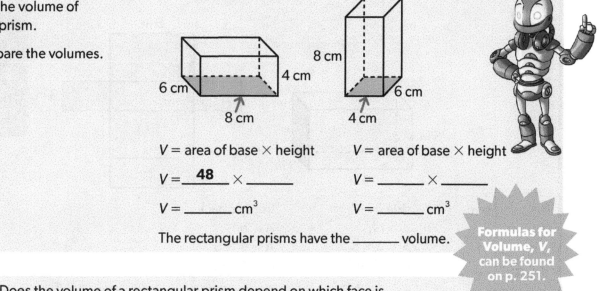

8 cm
4 cm
6 cm
8 cm

8 cm
6 cm
4 cm

V = area of base × height

$V = \underline{\textbf{48}} \times \underline{\hspace{1cm}}$

$V = \underline{\hspace{1cm}}$ cm^3

V = area of base × height

$V = \underline{\hspace{1cm}} \times \underline{\hspace{1cm}}$

$V = \underline{\hspace{1cm}}$ cm^3

The rectangular prisms have the _____ volume.

Formulas for Volume, V, can be found on p. 251.

DISCUSS Does the volume of a rectangular prism depend on which face is used as the base? Use examples to support your thinking.

PRACTICE

Find the volume of the rectangular prism.

1
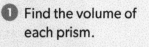
8 in.
6 in.
20 in.
_____

2
5 cm
10 cm
15 cm
_____

Find and compare the volumes of these rectangular prisms.

3
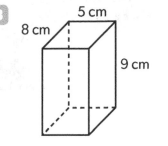
5 cm
8 cm
9 cm

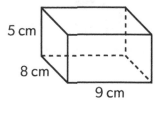
5 cm
8 cm
9 cm

_____

You can find the **surface area** of an object by finding the sum of the areas of all of its faces, or exterior surfaces. Make a net of the object to see all the faces.

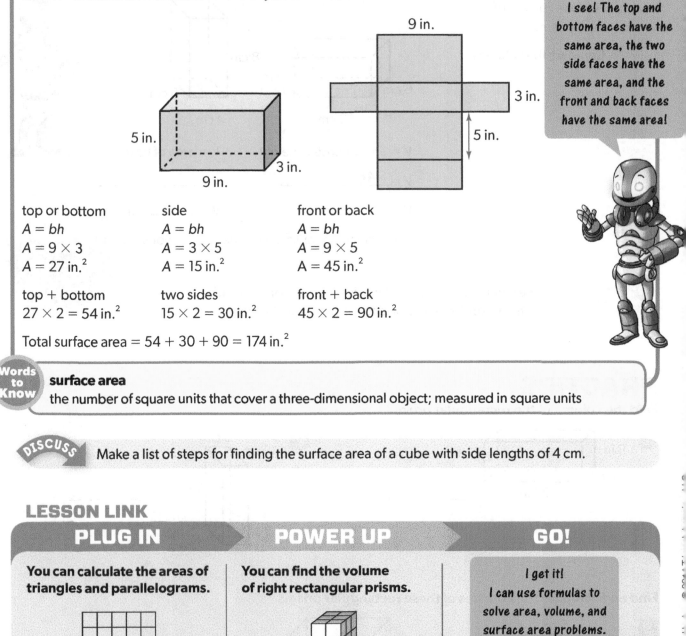

9 in.

3 in.

5 in.

5 in.

9 in.

3 in.

> I see! The top and bottom faces have the same area, the two side faces have the same area, and the front and back faces have the same area!

top or bottom	side	front or back
$A = bh$	$A = bh$	$A = bh$
$A = 9 \times 3$	$A = 3 \times 5$	$A = 9 \times 5$
$A = 27$ in.^{2}	$A = 15$ in.^{2}	$A = 45$ in.^{2}
top + bottom	two sides	front + back
$27 \times 2 = 54$ in.^{2}	$15 \times 2 = 30$ in.^{2}	$45 \times 2 = 90$ in.^{2}

Total surface area = $54 + 90 + 90 = 174$ in.^{2}

Total surface area = $54 + 30 + 90 = 174$ in.^{2}

Words to Know

surface area
the number of square units that cover a three-dimensional object; measured in square units

DISCUSS Make a list of steps for finding the surface area of a cube with side lengths of 4 cm.

LESSON LINK

PLUG IN	POWER UP	GO!
You can calculate the areas of triangles and parallelograms.	**You can find the volume of right rectangular prisms.**	I get it! I can use formulas to solve area, volume, and surface area problems.

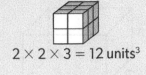

$2 \times 2 \times 3 = 12$ units^3

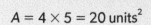

$A = 4 \times 5 = 20$ units^2

WORK TOGETHER

You can find the capacity of an object, or how much it holds, by calculating its volume.

- You need to find the volume of the vase.

- Use a formula to find the volume of the triangular prism.

  V = area of triangular base $\times$ height of prism

  $V = \left(\frac{1}{2} \text{ base} \times \text{height}\right) \times \text{height of prism}$

The glass vase can hold 2,160 cubic inches of water.

How much water will fill this vase, which is a triangular prism?

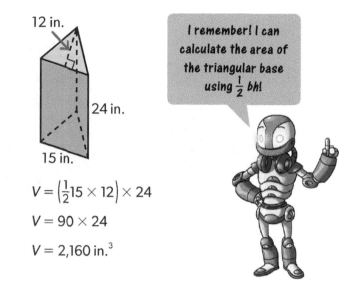

12 in.

24 in.

15 in.

$V = \left(\frac{1}{2}15 \times 12\right) \times 24$

$V = 90 \times 24$

$V = 2{,}160 \text{ in.}^3$

I remember! I can calculate the area of the triangular base using $\frac{1}{2} bh$!

A Use reasoning to solve a problem involving surface area.

DO

Six cubes with edges measuring 4 in. each are glued together. What is the total surface area to be painted?

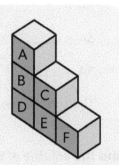

1 Find the area of one face.

2 Count the number of faces of each cube that need paint.

$A = bh =$ _____ $\times$ _____ $=$ _____ in.^{2}

Faces to be painted:

3 Add the total number of faces.

A	B	C	D	E	F
5	_____	_____	_____	_____	_____

4 Multiply the area of one face by the number of faces to be painted.

Total number of faces: _____

Total surface area = _____ $\times$ _____ $=$ _____ in.^{2}

DISCUSS

Aaron wants to build a ramp out of concrete. What measurements does he need? Explain why.

PRACTICE

Find the surface area of the prism.

1

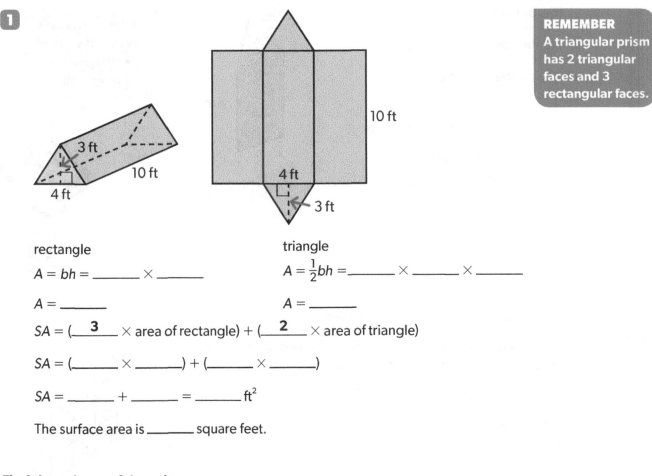

10 ft

3 ft

10 ft

4 ft

4 ft

3 ft

rectangle

$A = bh = $ _____ $\times$ _____

$A = $ _____

triangle

$A = \frac{1}{2}bh = $ _____ $\times$ _____ $\times$ _____

$A = $ _____

$SA = ($ __**3**__ $\times$ area of rectangle$) + ($ __**2**__ $\times$ area of triangle$)$

$SA = ($ _____ $\times$ _____ $) + ($ _____ $\times$ _____ $)$

$SA = $ _____ $+$ _____ $=$ _____ ft^2

The surface area is _____ square feet.

Find the volume of the prism.

2

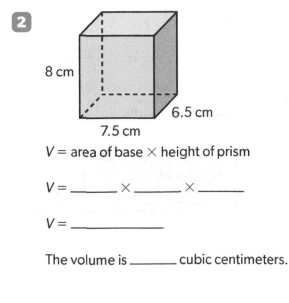

8 cm

6.5 cm

7.5 cm

$V = $ area of base $\times$ height of prism

$V = $ _____ $\times$ _____ $\times$ _____

$V = $ _____

The volume is _____ cubic centimeters.

3

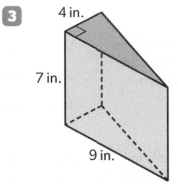

4 in.

7 in.

9 in.

$V = $ area of triangular base $\times$ height of prism

$V = ($ _____ $\times$ _____ $\times$ _____ $) \times$ _____

$V = $ _____ $\times$ _____

$V = $ _____

The volume is _____ cubic inches.

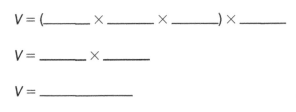

These blocks are cubes glued together and will be painted. Find the total surface area to be painted.

4

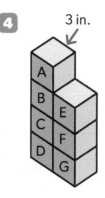

3 in.

Area of one face: _____

Number of faces to be painted: _____

Total surface area to be painted: _____

Find the volume.

5 Triangular prism:

base of triangle = 3 m

height of triangle = 7 m

height of prism = 8 m

Volume: _____

6 Rectangular prism:

length = 2 ft

width = 3 ft

height = 5 ft

Volume: _____

Solve.

7 A triangle has an area of 9 square feet. The height is 6 ft. What is the length of the base?

_____

I can draw and label a diagram to understand the problem.

8 A triangular prism has a volume of 1,080 cm^3. The base of the triangle is 15 cm and its height is 8 cm. What is the height of the prism?

_____

DISCUSS

See the Relationship

Hannah and a friend ate ice cream from a carton shaped like a rectangular prism. The carton had a length of 7 in., a width of 5 in., and a height of 3.5 in. After they ate, the carton was still $\frac{3}{4}$ full. Hannah wanted to find the volume of ice cream eaten. Here are her computations.

Volume of carton:

$V = 7 \times 5 \times 3.5$

$V = 122.5$ in.^{3}

The volume of the carton is 122.5 in.^{3}

Volume of ice cream eaten:

$V = 122.5 \times \frac{3}{4}$

$V = 91.88$ in.^{3}

They ate 91.88 in.^{3} of ice cream.

What was Hannah's error? What is the correct answer?

PROBLEM SOLVING

A NEW FLOOR

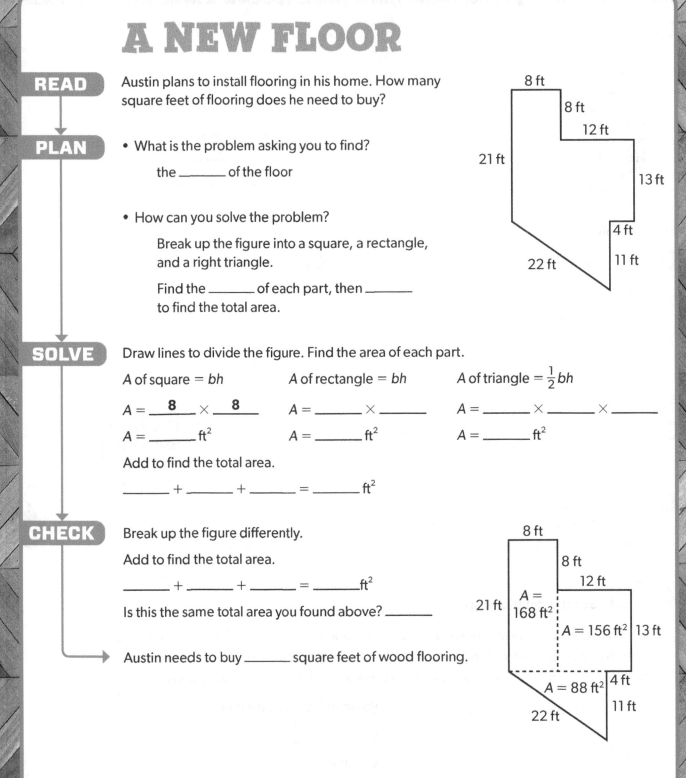

READ

Austin plans to install flooring in his home. How many square feet of flooring does he need to buy?

PLAN

• What is the problem asking you to find?

the _____ of the floor

• How can you solve the problem?

Break up the figure into a square, a rectangle, and a right triangle.

Find the _____ of each part, then _____ to find the total area.

SOLVE

Draw lines to divide the figure. Find the area of each part.

A of square = bh A of rectangle = bh A of triangle = $\frac{1}{2}bh$

$A = \underline{\quad 8 \quad} \times \underline{\quad 8 \quad}$ $A = \underline{\quad\quad} \times \underline{\quad\quad}$ $A = \underline{\quad\quad} \times \underline{\quad\quad} \times \underline{\quad\quad}$

$A = \underline{\quad\quad} \text{ft}^2$ $A = \underline{\quad\quad} \text{ft}^2$ $A = \underline{\quad\quad} \text{ft}^2$

Add to find the total area.

$\underline{\quad\quad} + \underline{\quad\quad} + \underline{\quad\quad} = \underline{\quad\quad} \text{ft}^2$

CHECK

Break up the figure differently.

Add to find the total area.

$\underline{\quad\quad} + \underline{\quad\quad} + \underline{\quad\quad} = \underline{\quad\quad} \text{ft}^2$

Is this the same total area you found above? _____

Austin needs to buy _____ square feet of wood flooring.

PRACTICE

Use the problem-solving steps to help you.

I have to make sure to include the correct units.

1 Miguel plans to paint a wood deck. He needs to buy the correct amount of paint. What is the area of the deck? If one can of paint covers 250 square feet, how many cans of paint should Miguel buy?

CHECKLIST
- [ ] READ
- [ ] PLAN
- [ ] SOLVE
- [ ] CHECK

2 Isabel wants to make a new cover for her tent. How much material does she need? If the material costs $22.00 per square meter, how much will it cost Isabel to make the cover?

CHECKLIST
- [ ] READ
- [ ] PLAN
- [ ] SOLVE
- [ ] CHECK

3 Oliver built a mailbox and wants to know exactly how much it can hold. What is the total volume of the mailbox?

CHECKLIST
- [ ] READ
- [ ] PLAN
- [ ] SOLVE
- [ ] CHECK

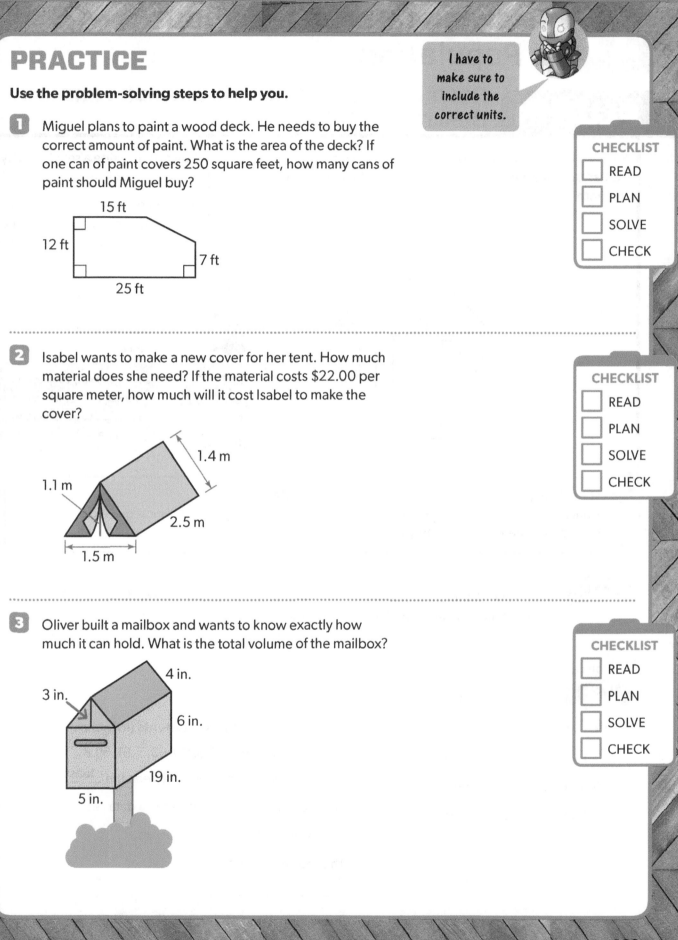

17 Drawing Inferences about a Population

PLUG IN — Recognizing Statistical Questions and Describing Data

You can learn information about a group of individuals by asking a **statistical question**. The answers given by the individuals are the **data**.

You can describe a set of data by its center and spread.

The center can be measured as the mean, median, or mode. The spread can be described by the range of the data.

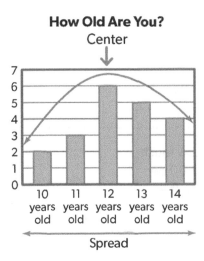

How Old Are You?

Center

Spread

mean age: 12.3 years
median: 12 years
mode: 12 years
range: 4 years

With so many responses, it's helpful to find values or terms to describe the entire data set.

Words to Know

statistical question
a question asked about a group that could have many different possible responses

data
the responses to a statistical question

DISCUSS

Martin asks the following question: "Did Mrs. Watkins assign homework last night?" Is this a statistical question? Explain why or why not.

A You can describe the spread of a data set by the range.

DO Find the range of the data set.

1 Define range.

2 Identify the greatest value.

3 Identify the least value.

4 Subtract. Write the range.

Heights of 7th grade students (in inches)

62.4, 58.8, 62, 60.5, 60, 63.5, 61, 59.8

The range is the difference between the _____**least**_____

and the _____ values in a data set.

The tallest height is _____ inches.

The shortest height is _____ inches.

_____ – _____ = _____

The range of the heights is _____ inches.

A data set can have no mode if all data values appear the same number of times.

B You can calculate the measures of center of a data set.

DO Find the mean, median, and mode of the data set.

1 To find the mean, first add the data values. Then divide the sum by the number of data values.

2 To find the median, first order the data values from least to greatest. Then find the middle value.

3 To find the mode, identify the value that appears most often in the set.

**Landville Animal Shelter,
Kitten Weight Records, March 23**

Kitten Name	Weight
Smokey	1.8 pounds
Ginger	1.4 pounds
Socks	1.9 pounds
Miss Kitty	1.7 pounds
Pickles	2.0 pounds
Tiger	1.9 pounds
Ralph	1.9 pounds

$1.8 + 1.4 + 1.9 + 1.7 + 2.0 + 1.9 + 1.9 =$ _____ pounds

_____ ÷ _____ = _____ pounds

The mean weight is _____ pounds.

Least to greatest:

_____, _____, _____, _____, _____, _____, _____

The median is _____ pounds.

The mode is _____ pounds.

DISCUSS Suppose there are two middle values in a data set. How can you find the median of the data set?

PRACTICE

Find the range of the data set.

1 0, 1, 2, 3, 4, 5, 8, 8, 9, 10

Range: __**10**__

2 1.8, 10.4, 3.2, 10.5, 9.5

Range: _____

Find the mean, median, and mode of the data set.

3 0.3, 0.4, 0.7, 0.8, 0.8, 0.9, 1.7

Mean: __**0.8**__

Median: _____

Mode: _____

4 10, 15, 18, 35, 37, 47, 49, 78, 107

Mean: _____

Median: _____

Mode: _____

Identifying a Representative Sample of a Population

You can use part of a data set to learn about the entire data set.

What is the average height of everyone in the United States?

It would be very difficult to collect the height of every person.

There are more than 300 million people in the United States. There has to be another way to find out about the data set!

You can collect a **representative sample** to learn about the entire **population**.

Collect the heights of 1,000 people who are representative of the population of the United States.

I get it! Learning about a small group can tell me about the larger group that they are part of.

Words to Know

population
an entire group of individuals of interest

Example:
all automobile drivers in the United States

representative sample
a part of the population that is large enough, selected at random, and similar in qualities to the entire population

Example:
5,000 randomly selected drivers throughout the United States

DISCUSS How could you find a representative sample of the players in a softball league?

A You can identify a population and a representative sample.

DO

The marching band is ordering T-shirts to sell to classmates. The members need to know how many small, medium, and large shirts they expect to sell. They will ask 100 randomly selected students, "What size T-shirt do you wear?" Find the population and representative sample.

1 Identify the population.

The population is __all of the students at the school__.

2 Identify the representative sample.

The representative sample is

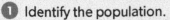

_____

A sample is representative only if it tells you about the entire population.

B You can identify whether a sample is representative of a population.

DO

An application developer wants to know whether smartphone users in the United States would be interested in a movie-review application. The company will randomly select 1,000 smartphone users in California. Is this a representative sample?

1. Identify the population.

2. Identify the sample.

3. Determine whether or not the sample is representative.

The population is _____.

The sample is **1,000 randomly selected smartphone users in California** _____.

Is this sample representative? Explain.

_____

DISCUSS

A tea company holds taste tests for U.S. customers to compare its product to other energy drinks on the market. How can it conduct a taste test using a representative sample of the entire population?

PRACTICE

Identify the population and the sample.

1 A local restaurant wants to know if its customers like its new menu. It surveys 100 randomly selected customers over one week.

Population: **all customers** _____

Sample: _____

2 A company makes 10,000 baseball caps a week. Each day, 500 caps are randomly selected for inspection.

Population: _____

Sample: _____

3 A scientist studies the water quality at five rivers throughout the United States to find out about the water quality of all rivers in the United States.

Population: _____

Sample: _____

4 A company wants to know if its employees are spending too much time writing personal e-mail during the workday. So, every hundredth e-mail that is sent will be reviewed.

Population: _____

Sample: _____

Is the sample representative? Explain.

5 The librarian at a middle school wants to know how many books students borrow from the library. She asks a randomly selected group of 6th graders to answer some questions.

_____

_____

6 A stadium manager wants to know if fans think ticket prices are too high. She asks 10 fans at the game what they think about ticket prices.

_____

_____

Drawing Inferences about a Population

To make a conclusion about a population from part of the population, start by collecting a representative sample.

Scientists want to know the average birth weight of a panda. They track the birth weights of randomly selected pandas around the world. They calculate the average weight of the sample to be 3.5 ounces.

> Weighing randomly selected baby pandas around the world means they will be representative of all baby pandas.

You can use the information from a representative sample to describe an entire population.

Because scientists used a representative sample, they can conclude that the average birth weight of all pandas is 3.5 ounces.

This kind of a conclusion is called an **inference**.

> I get it! Representative samples tell me something about the population.

Words to Know

inference

a logical conclusion, which may be based on a representative sample

If a representative sample chosen at random of one restaurant's hamburgers indicates each weighs about $\frac{1}{4}$ pound, you may conclude that all of the restaurant's hamburgers weigh about $\frac{1}{4}$ pound each.

DISCUSS You and five friends saw a movie last weekend. If none of you liked the movie, can you infer that no one liked that movie? Why?

LESSON LINK

PLUG IN	POWER UP	GO!
Mean, median, mode, and range describe data or the responses to statistical questions.	**You can identify a representative sample of a population.**	I see! I can use the results of a representative sample, including mean, median, mode, and range, to make inferences about a population.
Data set: 2, 2, 2, 4, 5 Mean: 3 Median: 2 Mode: 2 Range: 3	Population: all customers of one department store Representative sample: every 100th customer of the department store	

WORK TOGETHER

You can make inferences about populations using representative samples.

- The population is all registered voters.

- A random sample of 1,000 voters is used.

- Using the poll data, researchers can infer that Candidate A will win the election before all the votes are counted.

An exit poll is a survey taken by a randomly selected group of voters after they have voted. These surveys may include several questions, but they would include which candidate each voter selected.

In one state's election for governor, all registered voters may participate. An exit poll is taken of 1,000 voters. 50% chose Candidate A, 30% chose Candidate B, and 20% chose Candidate C. The mode of the votes is for Candidate A.

> I get it! The measures of center from a representative sample let me make inferences about the entire population.

A You can make an inference using a representative sample.

The owner of a shoe store took a representative sample of his customers. He asked every 20th customer about his or her shoe purchases. More than half of the people said they would pay more than $200 for a new style of shoe. Should the owner sell the new style of $250 shoes?

1 Identify the population.

The population is _____.

2 Identify the sample.

The sample is _____.

3 Make an inference.

The store owner can infer about the population that

_____

_____

_____.

DISCUSS Is an inference from a representative sample always true about the population?

PRACTICE

Identify the population and sample. Can an inference be made?

1 A new medicine is being tested for treatment of asthma in adults. A random sample of 1,500 adult men with asthma will take the medicine to see its effect.

Population: **all adults with asthma** _____

Sample: _____

Can an inference be made? Explain.

_____

_____

_____

_____

_____

> **REMEMBER**
> I have to make sure a sample includes information about all types of people present in the population for it to be representative.

2 A car company must test all of its vehicles' safety. During one month, the company randomly tests 500 cars from one of its five models. The test results indicate this model of car is safe in a low-speed crash.

Population: _____

Sample: _____

Can an inference be made? Explain.

_____

_____

_____

_____

_____

3 The owner of a supermarket chain wants to reduce the number of plastic bags the stores uses. She has a survey in which every 1,000th customer at each store is offered paper bags instead of plastic bags. The survey shows that 80% of these customers prefer paper bags.

Population: _____

Sample: **every 1,000th customer at each store** _____

Can an inference be made? Explain.

_____

_____

_____

_____

> **HINT**
> To find if a sample is representative, ask yourself: Is each member of the population just as likely to be included in the sample?

Can an inference be made based on this sample? Explain.

I can make an inference only if the sample is representative.

4 Population: barn owls in the United States
Sample: a randomly selected group of 50 barn owls
from North Carolina

_____

_____

_____

5 Population: all teenagers in Idaho
Sample: a randomly selected group of 1,000 teenagers
in Idaho

_____

_____

_____

See the Connection

I remember!
I can apply the measures
of center from a
representative sample to
the entire population!

Max wants to know the average height of all NBA basketball
players. There are 430 players in the league.

How can he find the average height without adding up the
heights of all 430 players?

PROBLEM SOLVING

MAKING MORE MUSIC

READ

A music company president believes that teenagers listen to the radio more than any other age group. If this is true, the company would release singles by three new teenage bands. The company called a random selection of 1,000 radio listeners around the country. It found that 50% are 13- to 19-year-olds, 10% are 12 or younger, and 40% are 20 or older. How can the music company president find out if she is correct?

PLAN

• What is the problem asking you to find?

If _____ listen to the radio more than any other age group

• What do you need to know to solve the problem?

The population is _____.

The sample of the population is _____.

• How can you solve the problem?

Decide if the sample is representative of the population and make an inference.

SOLVE

Was the sample representative? How can you tell?

_____

Can you make an inference? Why or why not?

_____

What can the company conclude about radio listeners?

_____

CHECK

Review the population, the sample, and the inference.

Was the music company president correct?

_____

_____

PRACTICE

Can an inference be made? If so, what is it? If not, why not? Use the problem-solving steps to help you.

1 Principal Jennings thinks the school should have a jazz band. He goes to the morning band class and asks the students if they're interested in being in a jazz band. Out of 30 students, only three say they're interested. Principal Jennings decides not to survey any of the other three band classes.

CHECKLIST
- [ ] READ
- [ ] PLAN
- [ ] SOLVE
- [ ] CHECK

2 Jackie wants to find out the average length of a word in the book she has just finished reading. She opens the book to a random page and points to a word without looking. Then she writes down the number of letters in that word. She does this 100 times. She finds that the average length of a word on her list is 6 letters.

CHECKLIST
- [ ] READ
- [ ] PLAN
- [ ] SOLVE
- [ ] CHECK

3 A town wants to add lights to its little league fields so it can have night games. It surveyed a random sample of people in the town to see if they would be interested in night games. Here are the results:

Very interested: 33%
Somewhat interested: 42%
Not interested: 20%
Not sure: 5%

CHECKLIST
- [ ] READ
- [ ] PLAN
- [ ] SOLVE
- [ ] CHECK

18 Making Predictions with Experimental Probability

PLUG IN   Probability

The likelihood that a particular outcome will occur is called its **probability**.

Find the probability of the spinner landing on 1.

> I see the sections are the same size, so each section is equally likely to occur!

1 **Count the number of possible outcomes.**

There are 6 equal-sized sections labeled 1 through 6.
There are 6 possible outcomes.

2 **Count the number of favorable outcomes.**

There is one section labeled 1.
There is 1 favorable outcome.

3 **Find the probability.**

$$\frac{\text{number of favorable outcomes}}{\text{number of possible outcomes}} = \frac{1}{6}$$

Words to Know

probability

the likelihood that a particular outcome will occur; a number between 0 and 1

The probability that a coin will land on heads is $\frac{1}{2}$.

DISCUSS

Would you expect to get the same probability if the spinner had 10 equal-sized sections numbered 1 through 10?

A Find the probability of an outcome.

DO

What is the probability of this spinner landing on a 2?

1 Count the number of possible outcomes.

2 Count the number of favorable outcomes.

3 Write the probability as a fraction.

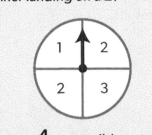

There are ____4____ possible outcomes.

There are _____ favorable outcomes.

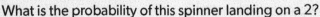

$$\frac{\text{number of favorable outcomes}}{\text{number of possible outcomes}} = \frac{\boxed{}}{\boxed{}}$$

If an event is impossible, the probability is 0. If an event is certain, the probability is 1.

B You can describe outcomes.

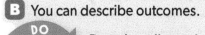

Dorothy rolls an eight-sided die that has the numbers 1 through 8 on its sides. Each side of the die is the same size. Find the probability that Dorothy will roll a 4. Describe this outcome as *impossible, certain, likely, unlikely,* or *equally likely.*

❶ Count the number of possible outcomes.

There are _____ possible outcomes.

❷ Count the number of favorable outcomes.

There is __1__ favorable outcome.

❸ Write the probability as a fraction.

$$\frac{\text{number of favorable outcomes}}{\text{number of possible outcomes}} = \frac{\boxed{}}{\boxed{}}$$

❹ Describe the outcome.

This outcome is _____.

DISCUSS

What must be true about the number of favorable outcomes and the number of possible outcomes for an outcome to be certain? Give an example.

PRACTICE

The table shows the number of marbles of each color in a bag. Use the data for problems 1–7.

❶ What is the probability of picking a red marble?

_____

Color	Number of Marbles
Green	8
Red	40
Blue	2

❷ What is the probability of picking a blue marble?

_____

❸ What is the probability of picking a green marble?

_____

Describe each outcome as *impossible, certain, likely, unlikely,* or *equally likely.*

❹ Picking a red marble is _____.

❺ Picking a blue marble is _____.

❻ Picking a green marble is _____.

❼ Picking a white marble is _____.

Finding Experimental Probability

You can conduct an experiment to determine the **experimental probability**. Experimental probability is based on actual outcomes.

Leo put 7 tiles that showed a letter from A through G into a bag. He picked one tile from the bag. After replacing the tile, he picked another. Leo recorded his results in the table. Find the experimental probability of Leo selecting the E tile on his next pick.

Letter	Number of Times
A	1
B	2
C	4
D	7
E	5
F	1
G	0

1 **Count the number of trials.**

Find the sum of the number of times a tile was picked.

$1 + 2 + 4 + 7 + 5 + 1 + 0 = 20$

2 **Count the number of favorable outcomes.**

Leo picked the E tile 5 times.

3 **Write the probability.**

$\dfrac{\text{number of favorable outcomes}}{\text{number of trials}} = \dfrac{5}{20} = \dfrac{1}{4}$

4 **Write the probability as a decimal.**

$\dfrac{1}{4} = 1 \div 4 = 0.25$

The experimental probability of picking the E tile is $\dfrac{1}{4}$ or 0.25.

> I get it! The experimental probability uses past outcomes to predict the likelihood of future outcomes!

Words to Know

experimental probability

the ratio of the total number of times that the favorable outcome has occurred to the total number of trials performed

A cube is numbered 1 through 6. Roll it 100 times.
The number 1 comes up 15 times.
Experimental probability $P(1) = \dfrac{15}{100}$, 0.15, or 15%

DISCUSS

Before the experiment, Leo calculated the probability of picking the E tile to be $\dfrac{1}{7}$. How is this probability different from the experimental probability he found later?

A You can find the experimental probability.

DO

Tasha flipped a penny 100 times. The penny landed heads up 20 times and tails up 80 times. What is the experimental probability that the penny will land heads up on the next toss?

1 Count the number of trials.

There were ___100___ trials.

2 Count the number of favorable outcomes.

There were _____ favorable outcomes.

3 Write the probability as a fraction. Simplify if necessary.

$\dfrac{\text{number of favorable outcomes}}{\text{number of trials}} = \dfrac{\boxed{}}{\boxed{}} = \dfrac{\boxed{}}{\boxed{}}$

4 Write the probability as a decimal.

_____ ÷ _____ = _____

I see! When I calculate experimental probability, I consider only past outcomes.

B You can determine the experimental probability.

DO

Laura spun the spinner 10 times. The spinner landed on red 4 times and blue 3 times. The rest of the spins landed on yellow. What is the experimental probability of the spinner landing on yellow on her next spin?

1 Count the number of trials.

2 Find the number of favorable outcomes.

3 Simplify if necessary. Write the probability as a fraction.

4 Write the probability as a decimal.

There were _____ trials.

The spinner landed on red or blue _____ times.

$10 - \boxed{} = \boxed{}$

There were _____ favorable outcomes.

$$\frac{\boxed{}}{\boxed{}} = \underline{} \div \underline{} = \underline{}$$

DISCUSS

Fred and Norah flipped a coin to decide who would get the last dessert. Norah asked Fred to choose heads or tails. "I'll take heads. The last time I flipped a coin, it landed on heads. So the experimental probability of it landing on heads is 1!" Fred exclaimed. What did he mean?

PRACTICE

Bryan rolled a number cube 100 times. He recorded his results in the table.
Use the table for problems 1–3. Write the probability as a fraction and a decimal.

1 What is the experimental probability of rolling a 1?

$\frac{13}{100}$

2 What is the experimental probability of rolling a 3?

3 What is the experimental probability of rolling a 4?

Number	Number of Times Rolled
1	13
2	18
3	17
4	20
5	27
6	5

READY TO GO
Making Predictions with Experimental Probability

You can use experimental probability on a small number of trials to predict the number of times an outcome is expected to occur for a large number of trials.

Jason spun the spinner 10 times and recorded his results in the table. Use the experimental probability to predict the number of times the spinner would land on green if he were to spin it 100 times.

Color	Number of Times Landed On
Red	2
Blue	3
Green	4
Yellow	1

1 **Find the experimental probability of the outcome (10 trials).**

The experimental probability of the spinner landing on green:

$$\frac{\text{number of favorable outcomes}}{\text{number of trials}} = \frac{4}{10}$$

2 **Write the fraction as a decimal.**

$$\frac{4}{10} = 4 \div 10 = 0.4$$

3 **Multiply to predict the outcome of 100 trials.**

$$0.4 \times 100 = 40$$

Jason can expect that the spinner will land on green 40 times.

> I get it! To find the number of expected outcomes I multiply the experimental probability by the number of future trials.

DISCUSS
Explain how to predict the number of times the spinner will land on red if Jason completes 200 trials.

LESSON LINK

PLUG IN	POWER UP	GO!

You can calculate the probability of an event.

The probability of rolling a 6 on a number cube numbered 1 through 6 is $\frac{1}{6}$.

You can calculate the experimental probability using the data of an experiment.

You flip a coin 10 times, and it lands on heads 7 times.

The experimental probability of heads is $\frac{7}{10}$.

> I see! I can use the experimental probability of an outcome to predict the number of times the outcome will occur in the future.

WORK TOGETHER

Roll Number Cube 10 times. Record your results in the table.

Predict how many times you would roll each number if you rolled the number cube 100 times.

- Find the experimental probability of rolling each number.

- Multiply each probability by 100.

- Write your prediction in the table.

Sometimes, converting the fraction to a decimal makes the multiplication easier.

Number	Number of Outcomes	Probability	Prediction
1			
2			
3			
4			
5			
6			

Number Cube can be found on p. 245.

A You can use the experimental probability to make predictions.

DO

Lisa selected numbered tiles from a bag. She recorded her results in the table.

Number	1	2	3	4	5	6	7	8	9	10
Number of Times Selected	6	4	0	1	6	0	2	5	3	3

If she completes 300 more trials, predict the number of times she will select an even number.

1 Count the number of trials.

2 Add to find the number of favorable outcomes.

3 Write the probability as a fraction.

4 Multiply the probability by 300.

There were _____ trials.

The numbers _____ are all even numbers.

_____ + _____ + _____ + _____ + _____ = _____

Lisa selected an even number _____ times.

$$\frac{\text{number of favorable outcomes}}{\text{number of trials}} = \frac{\boxed{}}{\boxed{}}$$

$$\frac{\boxed{}}{\boxed{}} \times 300 = \frac{\boxed{}}{\boxed{}} = \_\_\_\_$$

DISCUSS

If the number of future trials increased from 300 to 600, would your prediction for the number of even tiles selected increase or decrease? Explain.

PRACTICE

Jamal placed the letters from the word PROBABILITY in a bag. He selected one letter and then placed the letter back in the bag. He repeated this process 110 times. Use this information for problems 1 and 2.

1 Predict the number of times Jamal will select the letter P.

Number of possible outcomes: __11__

Number of favorable outcomes: _____

Probability: $\dfrac{\boxed{}}{\boxed{}}$

Multiply by 110: $\dfrac{\boxed{}}{\boxed{}} \times 110 =$ _____

Jamal will pick the letter P _____ times.

HINT
You can use the probability (as well as the expected probability) to make predictions about future outcomes.

2 Predict the number of times Jamal will select the letter B.

Number of possible outcomes: _____

Number of favorable outcomes: _____

Probability: $\dfrac{\boxed{}}{\boxed{}}$

Multiply by 110: $\dfrac{\boxed{}}{\boxed{}} \times 110 =$ _____

Jamal will pick the letter B _____ times.

Kayla flipped a coin 50 times. She recorded her results in the table.

3 Predict the number of times the coin will land heads up, based on past trials, if she flips the coin 250 times.

Probability: $\dfrac{\boxed{30}}{\boxed{}} =$ _____

Multiply by 250: _____ × 250 = _____

REMEMBER
Find the experimental probability to make your prediction.

Side	Number of Outcomes
Heads	30
Tails	20

The coin will land heads up _____ times.

In the table below, Louis recorded the results of spinning a spinner 100 times. Next, he will spin the spinner 1,000 times. Use this information for problems 4–6.

4 Predict the number of times the spinner will land on red.

_____

Color	Number of Outcomes
Red	34
Green	46
Yellow	20

5 Predict the number of times the spinner will land on green.

_____

6 Predict the number of times the spinner will land on yellow.

_____

Solve.

I know! Multiply the probability by the number of trials.

7 The probability of Stacy making a free-throw shot is 0.35. If she takes 20 free-throw shots during practice, how many should she make? _____

8 The probability of winning a card game is 0.50. If you play the game 10 times, how many times should you win? _____

DISCUSS

Analyze

Becky says that the theoretical probability of an outcome and the experimental probability of the same outcome usually aren't equal. Her teacher asks if if there are any cases in which she could be sure they are equal. Becky draws the following spinner.

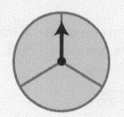

Calculate the theoretical probability of the outcome, and then think about the possible outcomes of experimental trials.

Do you agree with Becky? Explain.

PROBLEM SOLVING

WIN A LAPTOP

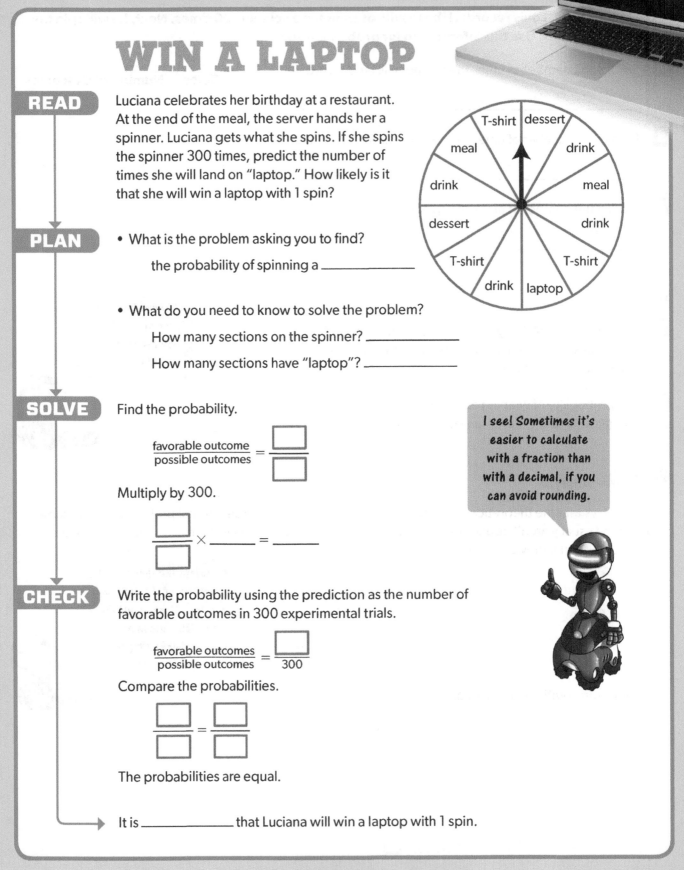

READ

Luciana celebrates her birthday at a restaurant. At the end of the meal, the server hands her a spinner. Luciana gets what she spins. If she spins the spinner 300 times, predict the number of times she will land on "laptop." How likely is it that she will win a laptop with 1 spin?

PLAN

• What is the problem asking you to find?

the probability of spinning a _____

• What do you need to know to solve the problem?

How many sections on the spinner? _____

How many sections have "laptop"? _____

SOLVE

Find the probability.

$$\frac{\text{favorable outcome}}{\text{possible outcomes}} = \frac{\boxed{}}{\boxed{}}$$

Multiply by 300.

$$\frac{\boxed{}}{\boxed{}} \times \underline{} = \underline{}$$

> I see! Sometimes it's easier to calculate with a fraction than with a decimal, if you can avoid rounding.

CHECK

Write the probability using the prediction as the number of favorable outcomes in 300 experimental trials.

$$\frac{\text{favorable outcomes}}{\text{possible outcomes}} = \frac{\boxed{}}{300}$$

Compare the probabilities.

$$\frac{\boxed{}}{\boxed{}} = \frac{\boxed{}}{\boxed{}}$$

The probabilities are equal.

It is _____ that Luciana will win a laptop with 1 spin.

PRACTICE

Find the probability. Then describe how likely the outcome is. Use the problem-solving steps to help you.

1 A sports store lets customers spin a spinner for a discount. Paul is buying a pair of sneakers. What is the probability of him getting at least 20% off the price of his new sneakers?

2 Vinia and Sang are on the track team. The coach will use a number cube to decide which of them should be the team captain. Vinia will be captain if she rolls an odd number. Otherwise, Sang will be captain. How likely is it for Vinia to be team captain?

I can calculate the probability for each of them to become team captain.

3 Rita hopes to win a phone case from a prize machine. The machine holds 40 prizes, and she will win one of these. The 40 prizes are 12 plastic rings, 9 plastic bracelets, 15 key chains, and 4 phone cases. How likely is she to win a phone case?

Probability Models

PLUG IN   Exploring Theoretical Probability

You can use **theoretical probability** to predict how often a die with 8 sides will land on an even number.

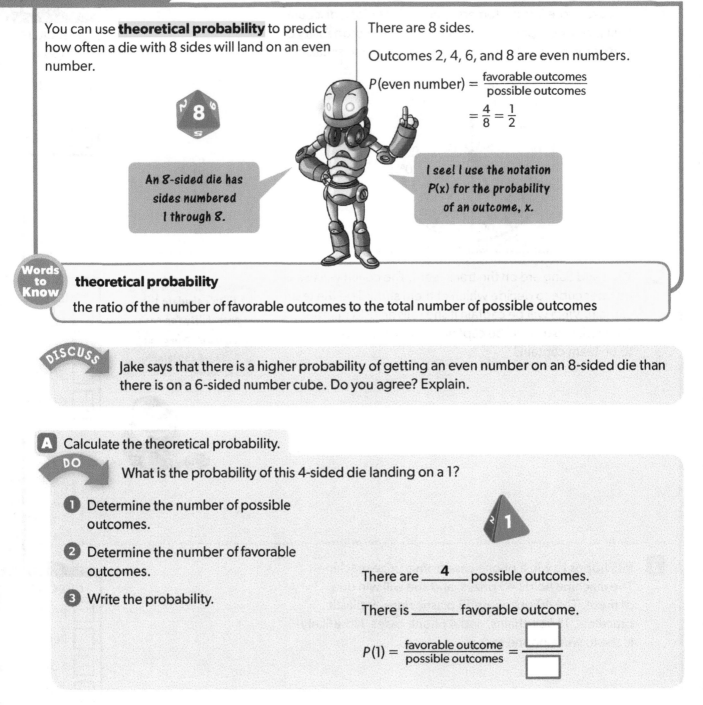

There are 8 sides.

Outcomes 2, 4, 6, and 8 are even numbers.

$$P(\text{even number}) = \frac{\text{favorable outcomes}}{\text{possible outcomes}}$$

$$= \frac{4}{8} = \frac{1}{2}$$

An 8-sided die has sides numbered 1 through 8.

I see! I use the notation P(x) for the probability of an outcome, x.

Words to Know

theoretical probability

the ratio of the number of favorable outcomes to the total number of possible outcomes

DISCUSS

Jake says that there is a higher probability of getting an even number on an 8-sided die than there is on a 6-sided number cube. Do you agree? Explain.

A Calculate the theoretical probability.

DO

What is the probability of this 4-sided die landing on a 1?

1 Determine the number of possible outcomes.

2 Determine the number of favorable outcomes.

3 Write the probability.

There are ____4____ possible outcomes.

There is _____ favorable outcome.

$$P(1) = \frac{\text{favorable outcome}}{\text{possible outcomes}} = \frac{\boxed{}}{\boxed{}}$$

B Use theoretical probability to predict the likelihood of a future event.

DO

What is the probability of getting a discount of more than 10% on this sale spinner?

I get it! "Free" is the same as a 100% discount.

❶ Determine the number of possible outcomes and favorable outcomes.

❷ Determine the probability. Write the probability as a fraction, decimal, and percent.

❸ Describe the likelihood. Use one of these terms: *likely, unlikely,* or *neither likely nor unlikely.*

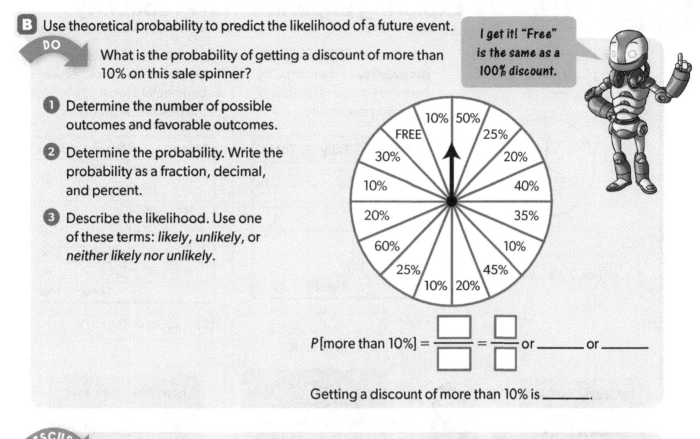

$P[\text{more than } 10\%] = \dfrac{\square}{\square} = \dfrac{\square}{\square}$ or _____ or _____

Getting a discount of more than 10% is _____.

DISCUSS

Hilda says getting a discount of 10% or greater on the wheel is 100%. Do you agree? Explain.

PRACTICE

Write the probability of spinning E on the spinner.

1

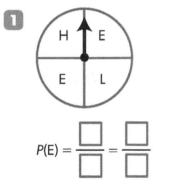

$P(E) = \dfrac{\square}{\square} = \dfrac{\square}{\square}$

2

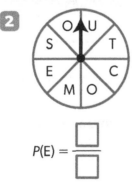

$P(E) = \dfrac{\square}{\square}$

3

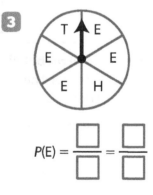

$P(E) = \dfrac{\square}{\square} = \dfrac{\square}{\square}$

Exploring Experimental Probability

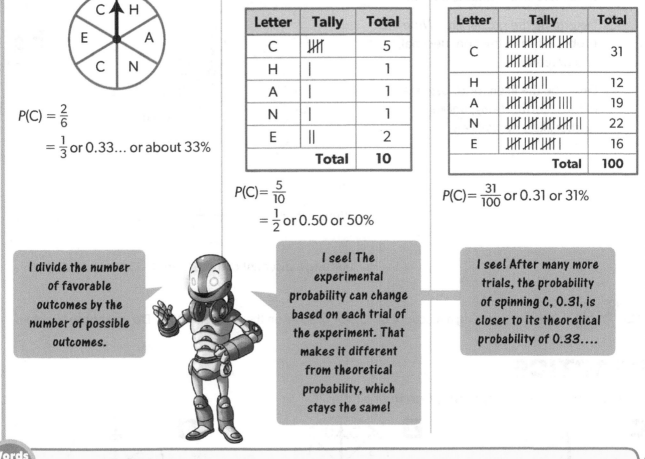

The theoretical probability of spinning C on this spinner is always the same.

$P(C) = \frac{2}{6}$

$= \frac{1}{3}$ or 0.33... or about 33%

I can find the **experimental probability** of spinning C by performing several trials and recording the results.

Letter	Tally	Total
C	卌	5
H	I	1
A	I	1
N	I	1
E	II	2
Total		**10**

$P(C) = \frac{5}{10}$

$= \frac{1}{2}$ or 0.50 or 50%

The more times you repeat the experiment, the closer the experimental probability will get to the theoretical probability.

Letter	Tally	Total
C	卌 卌 卌 卌 卌 卌 I	31
H	卌 卌 II	12
A	卌 卌 卌 IIII	19
N	卌 卌 卌 卌 II	22
E	卌 卌 卌 I	16
Total		**100**

$P(C) = \frac{31}{100}$ or 0.31 or 31%

I divide the number of favorable outcomes by the number of possible outcomes.

I see! The experimental probability can change based on each trial of the experiment. That makes it different from theoretical probability, which stays the same!

I see! After many more trials, the probability of spinning C, 0.31, is closer to its theoretical probability of 0.33....

Words to Know

experimental probability
the ratio of the total number of times that the favorable outcome has occurred to the total number of trials performed

Martin rolls a number cube 100 times. He rolls a 5 on 18 rolls.

The experimental probability of rolling a 5 is $\frac{18}{100}$, 0.18, or 18%.

DISCUSS

Mateo rolled a 6-sided number cube 12 times. He rolled a 6 on five of these rolls. He thinks there is something wrong with the number cube because he expected to roll a 6 on two of these rolls. Ting suggested that he roll it 200 times before making that decision. Do you agree with Ting? Explain.

A Find the experimental probability of an event from an experiment.

DO

Find the experimental probability of spinning Y.

① Use the table to determine the number of favorable outcomes and the total number of trials in the experiment.

② Write the experimental probability as a fraction, decimal, and percent.

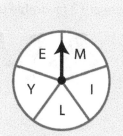

Letter	Tally	Total
E	IIII	4
M	卌	5
I	IIII	4
L	卌 I	6
Y	I	1
	Total	**20**

Number of favorable outcomes = _____

Number of trials in experiment = _____

$P(Y) = \dfrac{\text{number of favorable outcomes}}{\text{number of trials}}$

$= \dfrac{\boxed{}}{\boxed{}}$ or _____ or _____

DISCUSS

How would you describe how experimental probability and theoretical probability are different?

PRACTICE

Determine the experimental probability. Write the probability as fraction, decimal, and percent.

① What is P(D)?

Letter	Tally	Total
D	卌	5
O	卌 卌 卌 卌 卌	25
G	卌	5
W	卌	5
	Total	**40**

$P(D) = \dfrac{\text{number of favorable outcomes}}{\text{number of trials}}$

$= \dfrac{\boxed{}}{\boxed{40}}$

$= \dfrac{1}{\boxed{}}$ or _____ or _____

② What is P(O)?

Letter	Tally	Total
D	卌	5
O	卌 卌 卌 卌 卌	25
G	卌	5
W	卌	5
	Total	**40**

$P(O) = \dfrac{\text{number of favorable outcomes}}{\text{number of trials}}$

$= \dfrac{\boxed{}}{\boxed{40}}$

$= \dfrac{\boxed{}}{\boxed{}}$ or _____ or _____

READY TO GO | Probability Models

A drawer contains 2 green pairs of socks, 3 pink pairs, and 1 blue pair. Each pair is balled up together.

There are 6 possible outcomes.

In this case, the favorable outcome is a pink pair.

You can use a visual model to show the probability of picking a pink pair at **random**.

There are 3 favorable outcomes:

You can model six outcomes with a number cube, numbered 1 to 6.

Assign each pair of socks to a number on the cube.

1, 2, and 3 are the pink pairs.

4 is the blue pair.

5 and 6 are the green pairs.

$P(\text{pink}) = \frac{3}{6} = \frac{1}{2}$ or 0.5 or 50%

Words to Know

random
without a pre-selected goal

DISCUSS   Why do you think random selection is important in studying probability?

LESSON LINK

PLUG IN

You can calculate theoretical probability, which does not change based on past outcomes.

The theoretical probability of rolling an odd number on a number cube numbered 1 through 6 is $\frac{3}{6} = \frac{1}{2}$.

POWER UP

You can calculate experimental probability, which can change with each trial.

#	Total
Heads	140
Tails	160
Total	300

The experimental probability of tails from these 300 trials is

$\frac{160}{300} = \frac{8}{15}$, 0.533..., or ≈ 53%.

GO!

I get it! I can model outcomes by using either theoretical probability or experimental probability.

WORK TOGETHER

You can use a spinner to model the probability of picking a pair of pink socks from the drawer.

- The spinner shows the possible outcomes.
- The experimental probability is $\frac{3}{6}$ or $\frac{1}{2}$.
- The chart shows the results of 100 spins.
- The experimental probability is $\frac{42}{100}$ or $\frac{21}{50}$.

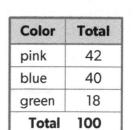

Color	Total
pink	42
blue	40
green	18
Total	**100**

$P(\text{pink}) = \frac{3}{6} = \frac{1}{2}$

$P(\text{pink}) = \frac{42}{100} = \frac{21}{50}$

A You can use a spinner to model probability.

DO

Armand has 12 golf shirts in a drawer. He has two each of the following colors: black, gray, green, navy, red, white. What is the probability of randomly choosing a navy shirt?

1 Make a spinner to show the outcomes.

2 The chart shows the results of 100 picks.

3 Calculate $P(\text{navy})$.

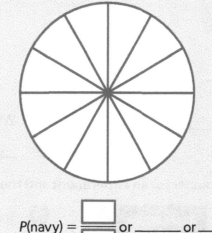

Color	Total
black	20
gray	15
green	14
navy	18
red	17
white	16
Total	**100**

$P(\text{navy}) = \dfrac{\square}{\square}$ or _____ or _____

DISCUSS

There are 15 boys and 13 girls in Ryan's class. Describe a model for finding the probability of randomly picking a boy from the class.

In my model, I have to make sure each of the possible outcomes is as likely as any other!

PRACTICE

Use the model for the situation to find the theoretical probability.

1 An ice cream machine randomly selects between 2 flavors.

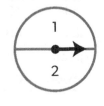

What is *P*(flavor 1)?

_____

2 Cars are manufactured in one of three randomly selected colors: blue, red, or green.

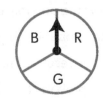

What is *P*(red car)?

_____

3 One of six contestants is randomly selected for the bonus prize.

What is *P*(contestant 1)?

_____

4 Campers are randomly assigned to one of 12 tents.

> **Hint**
> This die is numbered 1 through 12.

What is *P*(tent 1, 2, or 3)?

_____

Problems 5 and 6 show the spinner for an experiment and the results of the experiment.

5 Trevor models 9 outcomes on this spinner.

> **REMEMBER**
> The theoretical probability does not depend on trials.

What is *P*(A)?

_____

6 Trevor uses the model to create this chart.

Letter	Tally	Total
A	ⅢⅠ	6
B	|||	3
C	||	2
D	ⅢⅢ||	12
E	||||	4
F	|||	3
	Total	**30**

What is the experimental probability of landing of *A*?

_____

Use the results of the spinner to solve.

7 On Hank's model, each letter stands for a color of shirt he has. He has two navy blue shirts and one each of the following colors: silver, pink, indigo, emerald, and red. He will randomly select one shirt for Picture Day. He spins his model 130 times. Find P(R) with his model.

Letter	Tally	Total
S	卌 卌 IIII	14
P	卌 卌 卌 卌 卌	25
I	卌 卌 卌 卌 I	21
N	卌 卌 卌 卌 卌 卌 卌	35
E	卌 卌 卌 卌 II	22
R	卌 卌 III	13
	Total	**130**

fraction _____ decimal _____ percent _____

DISCUSS

Model Probabilities

Jules and Yolanda are going to use a spinner to model the color each might randomly select from a bag of gumdrops.

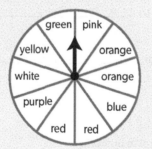

A model must include all of the outcomes. Each outcome must have the same probability of being selected as the situation it models.

Each makes a different table of 10 trials with the spinner. Do you expect the values in the two tables to be the same? Explain.

Each makes a new table of 100 trials. How do you expect the two tables to compare now?

PROBLEM SOLVING

MENU PROBABILITIES

READ

The restaurant where Austin works has a new menu. What model can Austin make to see if a randomly selected pizza from the menu will have meat? Then, use the model to find the theoretical probability the pizza will have meat.

PLAN

• What is the problem asking you to find?

Make a model for the list.

Find the _____ that the pizza will have meat.

• What do you need to know to solve the problem?

How many flavors are there? ___**8**___

How many flavors include meat? _____

PIZZA MENU

With Meat
Chicken
Seafood
Ham and Bacon
Pepperoni
New Sausage Supreme

Meatless
Double Cheese
Mushroom Madness
Vegetarian Deluxe

SOLVE

Make a model.

Assign each flavor to a _____.

$P(\text{meat}) = \dfrac{\boxed{}}{\boxed{}}$ or _____ or _____

CHECK

Use a formula.

$P(\text{meat}) = \dfrac{\text{number of favorable outcomes}}{\text{number of total outcomes}}$

$= \dfrac{\boxed{}}{\boxed{}}$ or _____ or _____

The probability is $\dfrac{\boxed{}}{\boxed{}}$, _____, or _____.

> If each outcome is as likely as any other, each outcome of the model should have an equal chance of being selected.

PRACTICE

Think of a model to show the probability. Show the probability as a fraction, decimal, and percent.

1 When working in the gym, Kayla randomly picks a workout station. What is the probability of her selecting the stair climber first?

Treadmill
Exercise bike
Abs machine
Stair climber
Free weights
Pool

2 Levi decides to randomly select a drink on the menu. What is the probability that he will pick a juice?

DRINKS MENU
Milk
Chocolate milk
Milk shake
Orange juice
Apple juice
Tomato juice
Coffee
Tea
Herbal tea

3 Amber chooses a card at random. What is the probability that she will pick a card with diamonds?

20 Tree Diagrams

PLUG IN Probability of Compound Events

A **compound event** includes two or more events not dependent on each other.

What is the probability of a quarter showing two heads on two flips in a row?

There are 4 possible outcomes.

HH, HT, TH, TT

There is 1 favorable outcome.

, HT, TH, TT

$$\text{Probability} = \frac{\text{number of favorable outcomes}}{\text{number of possible outcomes}}$$

$$P(2\text{ heads}) = \frac{1}{4}$$

Ok! The two events are the two coin flips. I can think of heads as H and tails as T.

I get it! I need to find the number of total outcomes, and also the number of favorable outcomes of both events happening together.

Words to Know

compound event

a combination of two or more events not dependent on each other

flipping a nickel and flipping a dime

DISCUSS Describe a compound event that includes three events.

A Find the probability of a compound event.

DO

What is the probability of one spinner landing on orange and then the other spinner landing on 2?

1. Find the possible outcomes.

2. Find the favorable outcomes.

3. Find the probability.

Possible outcomes:

P1, P2, P3, _____.

There are _____ possible outcomes.

There is _____ favorable outcome.

The probability of spinning orange and then 2 is $\dfrac{\square}{\square}$.

1
3   2

I see! I can use a table to list all possible outcomes of both events.

B You can find probabilities of compound events that have more than one favorable outcome.

DO

Use the spinners on p. 194. What is the probability that one spinner lands on purple and the other spinner lands on an odd number?

1 Use the table to find the total number of outcomes.

2 Find the possible outcomes.

3 Find the favorable outcomes.

4 Write the probability. Simplify if necessary.

		Spinner 2 Outcomes		
		1	2	3
Spinner 1 Outcomes	Purple	P1	P2	P3
	Orange	O1	O2	O3

There are _____ possible outcomes.

The favorable outcomes are _____ and _____.

There are _____ favorable outcomes.

The probability of spinning a purple and an

odd number is $\dfrac{\square}{\square} = \dfrac{\square}{\square}$.

DISCUSS

When calculating the outcomes of flipping two coins, Susan says there are only three possible outcomes, not four: two heads, two tails, or one of each. How would you explain the error to Susan?

PRACTICE

Find the probability.

1 Complete the table to show all of the possible outcomes when you flip a coin and then spin the spinner. What is the probability of showing tails and then spinning an even number?

		Spinner Outcomes			
		1	2	3	
Coin Flip Outcomes	H	H1			
	T		T2		

There are _____ possible outcomes.

What is the probability of showing tails and then spinning an odd number?

There are _____ favorable outcomes.

$P(\text{tails, then even number}) = \dfrac{\square}{\square} = \dfrac{\square}{\square}$

POWER UP — Sample Space of Compound Events

One way to show the **sample space** of a compound event is by using a **table of outcomes**.

Roll the number cube and then spin the spinner.

		Spinner Outcomes		
		1	**2**	**3**
	1	1, 1	1, 2	1, 3
	2	2, 1	2, 2	2, 3
Number Cube Outcomes	**3**	3, 1	3, 2	3, 3
	4	4, 1	4, 2	4, 3
	5	5, 1	5, 2	5, 3
	6	6, 1	6, 2	6, 3

I see! The table of outcomes shows each outcome once. Even though I could roll a number and spin a 1 two different ways, it is listed only once in the sample space.

The sample space has 18 outcomes.

Words to Know

sample space	**table of outcomes**
a list of possible outcomes of an event	a table showing the outcomes of an event

DISCUSS How might a table of outcomes help you determine the probability of flipping two heads?

A Make a list to show sample space.

DO What is the sample space for these two spinners?

1. List the first outcome from spinner 1 with each possible outcome from spinner 2.

2. List the second outcome from spinner 1 with each possible outcome from spinner 2.

3. Count the number of outcomes in the sample space.

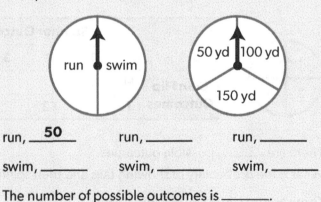

run, __50__   run, _____   run, _____

swim, _____   swim, _____   swim, _____

The number of possible outcomes is _____.

B Use a table of outcomes to calculate probability.

DO

What is the probability of spinning skip and then 150 yd on these exercise spinners?

> I can use S for skip and R for run.

❶ Complete the table of outcomes to find the sample space.

❷ Find P(skip, then 150 yd).

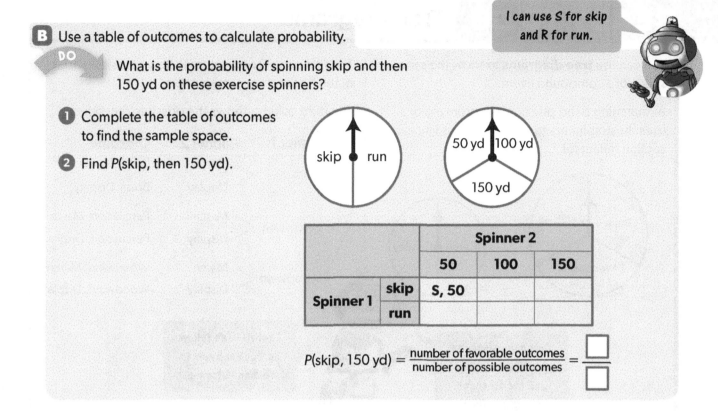

		Spinner 2		
		50	**100**	**150**
Spinner 1	**skip**	**S, 50**		
	run			

$$P(\text{skip, 150 yd}) = \frac{\text{number of favorable outcomes}}{\text{number of possible outcomes}} = \frac{\square}{\square}$$

DISCUSS

Tyler calculated P(skip or run, 100 yd or 150 yd). He said it was 50%. "No, it's 67%," corrected Jessica. Who is right? Explain.

PRACTICE

Complete the table of outcomes, then solve.

1 What is the probability of spinning run, swim, or bike, and then green team?

		Spinner 2		
		blue team (B)	**green team (G)**	**yellow team (Y)**
Spinner 1	**run (R)**			
	swim (S)			
	bike (B)			

$$P(\text{run or swim or bike, then green team}) = \frac{\square}{\square} = \frac{\square}{\square}$$

READY TO GO Tree Diagrams

You can use **tree diagrams** to show the sample space of a compound event.

At marching band practice, the drum major uses these spinners to select what activity each section rehearses.

The first and second columns show possible results of the first and second spinners.

The third column shows the possible outcomes.

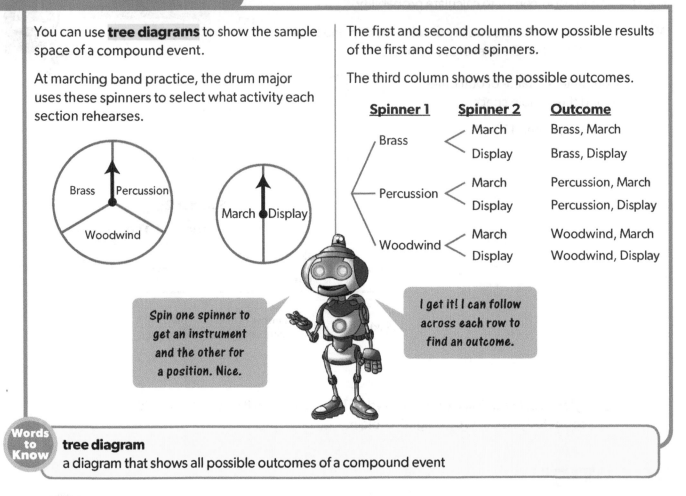

Spin one spinner to get an instrument and the other for a position. Nice.

I get it! I can follow across each row to find an outcome.

Words to Know

tree diagram
a diagram that shows all possible outcomes of a compound event

DISCUSS Lauren says she's not sure which spinner to list first when making her tree diagram. What would you tell her?

LESSON LINK

PLUG IN

You can calculate the probability of a compound event.

Flipping a coin and rolling a number cube:

H1, H2, H3, H4, H5, H6

T1, T2, T3, T4, T5, T6

$$P(H1) = \frac{1}{12}$$

POWER UP

You can use a table of outcomes to determine the sample space of a compound event.

		Spin 2	
		1	2
	A	A1	A2
Spin 1	B	B1	B2
	C	C1	C2

GO!

I get it! I can make a tree diagram to show the possible outcomes of an event or a compound event.

WORK TOGETHER

Use a tree diagram to show sample space.

- The first column shows the outcomes for Spinner 1.

- The second column shows the outcomes for Spinner 2.

- The third column shows the outcome of each compound event.

Spinner 1   **Spinner 2**

I see that every outcome is shown in the tree diagram.

Tree Diagram

Spinner 1	Spinner 2	Outcome
Brass	Solo	Brass, Solo
	Duet	Brass, Duet
Percussion	Solo	Percussion, Solo
	Duet	Percussion, Duet
Woodwind	Solo	Woodwind, Solo
	Duet	Woodwind, Duet

A Use a tree diagram to determine probability.

DO

What is the probability of flipping one heads and one tails, in any order?

1. Use a tree diagram to show the sample space.

2. Find the number of favorable outcomes.

3. Write the probability.

Flip 1	Flip 2	Outcome
Heads	Heads	
	Tails	
Tails	Heads	
	Tails	

I know that the outcome of each flip is equally likely. So the probability of each outcome is the same.

Number of favorable outcomes: _____

$$P(\text{heads and tails, in any order}) = \frac{\square}{\square} = \frac{\square}{\square}$$

DISCUSS

How would you draw a tree diagram for flipping a coin three times? How many outcomes will this produce?

PRACTICE

Make a tree diagram to show the sample space.

1 Spinner 1   Spinner 2

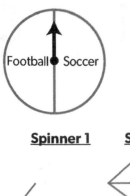 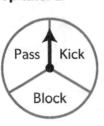

Spinner 1	Spinner 2	Outcome

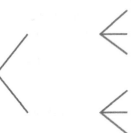

There are _____ outcomes.

2 Toss a number cube numbered 1 through 6 and then, without looking, pick a square or triangle from these two cards:

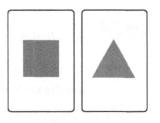

REMEMBER
Add a branch from each outcome of one toss to each outcome of the card pick.

There are _____ outcomes.

Solve.

3 What is the probability of being on the green soccer team?

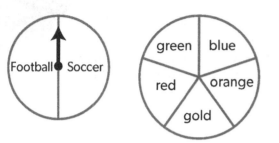

_____

4 What is the probability of rolling a cube numbered 1 through 6 twice and getting 1 each time?

_____

DISCUSS

Look for Patterns

Kyle sees a pattern in the probability of compound events. He says that you can multiply the number of outcomes of one spinner by the number of outcomes of the other spinner to find the probability of a compound event with two spinners.

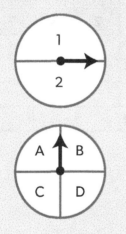

Find the probability from the first event and then from the second event.

What is the probability of getting a 1 and then an A?

The probability of getting 1 on the first spinner is:

_____

The probability of getting A on the first spinner is:

_____

Multiply the two probabilities—that is, the probability of 1 and then A.

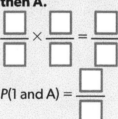

$P(1 \text{ and } A) = \dfrac{\square}{\square}$

There are different ways to calculate probability.

Think of a tree diagram for these events. Does Kyle's method make sense in this case? When do you think his method will work?

PROBLEM SOLVING

GET TO THE NEXT LEVEL

READ Megan is playing a video game, Race of the Robots, in which four robots finish a race in a random order. The robots are numbered 2, 5, 7, and 10. To get to the next level in a video game, Megan needs robot 2 to win two races in a row. What is the probability of her winning the game with the next 2 races?

PLAN
- What is the problem asking you to find?

  the probability of robot ___2___ winning race 1 and the

  probability of robot _____ winning race 2

- How can you find the probability?

  You can use a formula, a table of outcomes, or a tree diagram.

SOLVE Make a tree diagram or a table of outcomes.

Event 1   Event 2   Outcome

		Event 2			
		2	5	7	10
Event 1	2				
	5				
	7				
	10				

$P(2, \text{then } 2) = $ _____

CHECK Use a formula.

$$P = \frac{\text{number of favorable outcomes}}{\text{number of possible outcomes}} = \frac{\square}{\square}$$

The probability of Megan winning the game with the next 2 races is _____.

PRACTICE

Use the problem-solving steps to help you.

1 Tomas is playing a board game with a cube numbered 1 through 6. He has to roll a 5 and then another 5 to win. What is the probability of him winning on his next roll?

CHECKLIST
- [ ] READ
- [ ] PLAN
- [ ] SOLVE
- [ ] CHECK

2 A baker has 6 cookie cutters in a drawer: a square, two circles, a triangle, a heart, and a moon. He will pick one cookie cutter, put it back, and then select again. What is the probability of him picking a circle from the drawer twice in a row?

CHECKLIST
- [ ] READ
- [ ] PLAN
- [ ] SOLVE
- [ ] CHECK

3 To win the card game, Jada needs to pick a triangle card randomly from each row of five cards shown. What is the probability of Jada winning the game?

I see there are two triangles in the top row and one triangle in the bottom row.

CHECKLIST
- [ ] READ
- [ ] PLAN
- [ ] SOLVE
- [ ] CHECK

Glossary

additive inverses two numbers that are opposites, which have a sum of 0 (Lesson 5)

$$+9 \text{ and } -9 \text{ are additive inverses.}$$

area the number of equal-sized squares that cover the surface of a shape (Lesson 16)

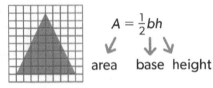

$$A = \tfrac{1}{2}bh$$

area   base height

area of a circle the total number of square units that fit inside the circle; The formula for the area of a circle is $A = \pi r^2$. (Lesson 15)

associative property a property of addition and multiplication that states that the grouping of the addends or factors does not affect the sum or product (Lesson 10)

$$(6 + 8) + 4 = 6 + (8 + 4)$$
$$(9 \times 2) \times 3 = 9 \times (2 \times 3)$$

circumference the distance around a circle, represented by C (Lesson 15)

circumference (C)

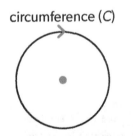

coefficient a number that multiplies a variable (Lesson 9)

commutative property a property of addition and multiplication that states that the order of the addends or factors does not affect the sum or product (Lesson 10)

$$85 + 94 = 94 + 85$$
$$15 \times 9 = 9 \times 15$$

compatible numbers numbers that are easy to compute mentally (Lesson 10)

complex fraction a fraction that has a fraction in the numerator, denominator, or both (Lessons 1 and 8)

$$\frac{7}{8} \div \frac{1}{3}$$

compound event a combination of two or more events not dependent on each other (Lesson 20)

constant of proportionality the constant ratio between two quantities in a proportional relationship (Lesson 2)

corresponding angles angles of two figures that are in the same relative positions (Lesson 14)

$$\angle M \text{ and } \angle X$$
$$\angle N \text{ and } \angle Y$$
$$\angle O \text{ and } \angle Z$$

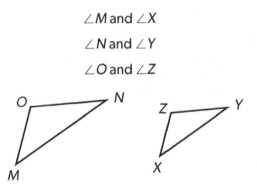

corresponding sides sides of two figures that are in the same relative positions (Lesson 14)

$$MN \text{ and } XY$$
$$NO \text{ and } YZ$$
$$OM \text{ and } ZX$$

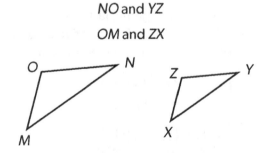

cross multiply multiply the numerator of each ratio by the denominator of the other ratio (Lesson 3)

$$\frac{m}{n} = \frac{2}{3}$$

cubic unit a unit used to measure volume (Lesson 16)

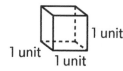

$$1 \text{ unit} \times 1 \text{ unit} \times 1 \text{ unit} = 1 \text{ unit}^3$$

data the responses to a statistical question (Lesson 17)

diameter a segment across a circle through its center, represented by d (Lesson 15)

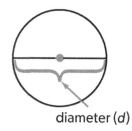

diameter (d)

distributive property a mathematical rule that states $a \times (b + c) = ab + ac$ and $a \times (b - c) = ab - ac$ (Lesson 9)

divisor the number by which another number is divided (Lesson 7)

$$\frac{2}{3} \div \frac{1}{3} = 2$$

divisor

equivalent expressions expressions that are equal in value and can be transformed into each other by using operations (Lesson 9)

$$4x + 8 = 4(x + 2)$$

equivalent ratios ratios with the same value that can be expressed as the same fraction in simplest form (Lesson 1)

Total Number of Seats	4	8	12	16	20
Number of Roller Coaster Cars	1	2	3	4	5

estimate to find a number that is close to an exact answer (Lesson 10)

experimental probability the ratio of the total number of times that the favorable outcome has occurred to the total number of trials performed (Lessons 18 and 19)

factor a number that is multiplied to get a product (Lesson 6)

$$4 \times -2 = -8$$

factor factor

greatest common factor (GCF) the largest integer and/or common variable that divides evenly into all of 2 or more terms (Lesson 9)

identity property a property of addition and multiplication that states that the sum of a number and zero is that number, and the product of a number and one is that number (Lesson 10)

$$175 + 0 = 175$$
$$89 \times 1 = 89$$

inequality a comparison of two expressions that uses one of these signs: $<$ (less than), $>$ (greater than), $\leq$ (less than or equal to), $\geq$ (greater than or equal to), or $\neq$ (not equal) (Lesson 13)

inference a logical conclusion, which may be based on a representative sample (Lesson 17)

inverse operation an operation that does the opposite of another (Lesson 12)

Multiplication is the inverse operation of division.

isolate to use inverse operations on both sides of an equation so the a variable is by itself on one side (Lesson 12)

$$t + 6 = 31$$
$$t + 6 - 6 = 31 - 6$$
$$t = 25$$

like terms terms in which the variables and any exponents on the variables are the same (Lesson 9)

$$3x + 6x + 7$$
$$\downarrow \qquad \downarrow$$
like terms

opposites two numbers that are the same distance from 0 but in opposite directions on a number line (Lesson 5)

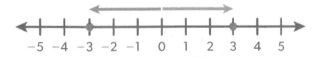

origin the point (0, 0) on a coordinate grid (Lesson 2)

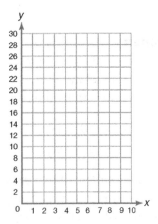

percent the number of parts out of every 100 equal parts (Lesson 3)

$$\frac{33}{100} = 33\%$$

percent proportion A comparison of a part of a whole to a part of 100 (Lesson 4)

$$\frac{\text{Part}}{\text{Whole}} = \frac{\text{Percent}}{100}$$

pi the ratio of the circumference of a circle to its diameter, $C \div d$; The symbol for pi is π. (Lesson 15)

$$\pi \approx 3.14$$

population an entire group of individuals of interest (Lesson 17)

probability the likelihood that a particular outcome will occur (Lesson 18)

The probability that a coin will land on heads is $\frac{1}{2}$.

product the answer in a multiplication problem (Lesson 6)

$$\frac{1}{3} \times \frac{1}{4} = \frac{1}{12}$$
$$\uparrow$$
product

proportion two ratios that are equivalent (Lessons 3 and 14)

proportional relationship a relationship in which the ratios being compared are equal (Lessons 2 and 3)

$$\frac{1}{2} = \frac{4}{8}$$

proportional sides corresponding sides with lengths that form equal ratios (Lesson 14)

$$\frac{MN}{XY} = \frac{NO}{YZ} = \frac{OM}{ZX}$$

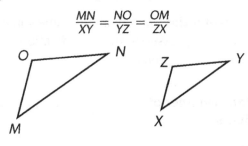

quotient the answer in a division problem (Lesson 7)

$$\frac{2}{3} \div \frac{1}{3} = 2$$

↑
quotient

radius a segment from the center of a circle to any point on it, represented by *r* (Lesson 15)

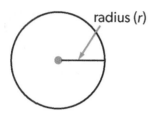

radius (*r*)

random without a pre-selected goal (Lesson 19)

rate a ratio that compares quantities with different units (Lesson 1)

$$\frac{150 \text{ miles}}{3 \text{ hours}}$$

ratio a comparison of two quantities (Lesson 1)

$$\frac{6}{5} \text{ or } 6:5 \text{ or } 6 \text{ to } 5$$

rational number a number that can be written as a ratio of two integers (Lesson 6)

reciprocals two numbers whose product is 1 (Lesson 7)

$$\frac{4}{5} \times \frac{5}{4} = 1$$

$\frac{4}{5}$ and $\frac{5}{4}$ are reciprocals.

representative sample a part of the population that is large enough, selected at random, and similar in qualities to the entire population (Lesson 17)

rounding approximating a number to its nearest place value (Lesson 10)

sample space a list of possible outcomes of an event (Lesson 20)

scale how much the actual object has been reduced or enlarged in a scale drawing (Lesson 14)

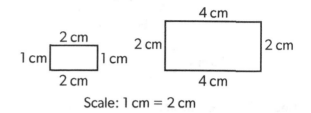

Scale: 1 cm = 2 cm

scale drawing a representation of an object that is proportional to the actual object (Lesson 14)

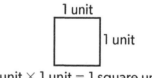

Scale: 1 cm = 0.5 cm

solution set the set of all numbers that make an inequality true (Lesson 13)

$$6x > 120$$

$$x > 20$$

square unit a unit used to measure area (Lesson 16)

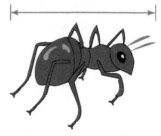

1 unit × 1 unit = 1 square unit

statistical question a question asked about a group that could have many different possible responses (Lesson 17)

surface area the number of square units that cover a three-dimensional object; measured in square units (Lesson 16)

table of outcomes a table showing the outcomes of an event (Lesson 20)

	Coin 2	
	H	**T**
Coin 1 **H**	H, H	H, T
T	T, H	T, T

theoretical probability the ratio of the number of favorable outcomes to the total number of possible outcomes (Lesson 19)

tree diagram a diagram that shows all possible outcomes of a compound event (Lesson 20)

unit rate a ratio that compares the number of units of one quantity to 1 unit of a second quantity (Lesson 1)

3 dollars per pound

$$\text{unit rate} = \frac{\text{dollars}}{\text{pound}} = \frac{\$3}{1\,\text{lb}}$$

volume the number of equal-sized cubes that fit inside a figure (Lesson 16)

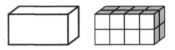

Volume = area of base x height

Math Tool: Fraction Strips

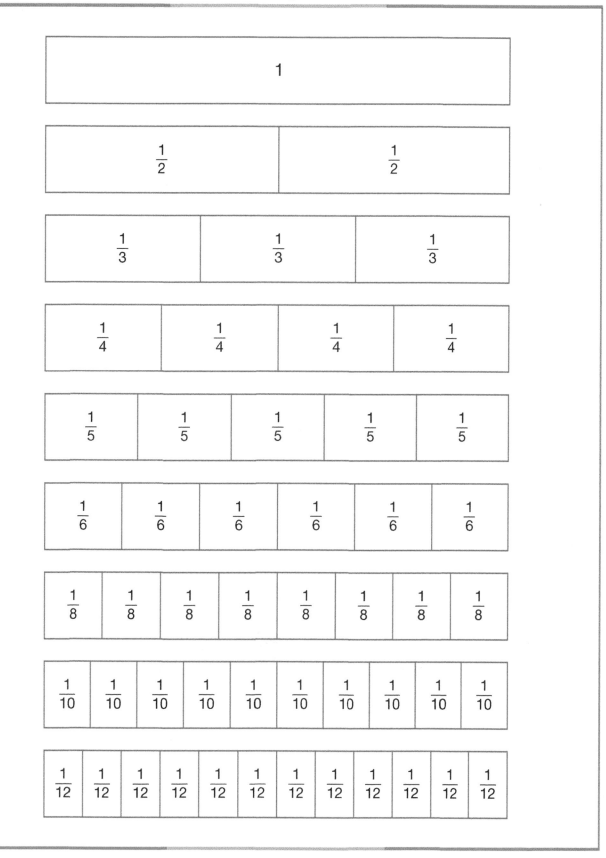

Math Tool: Fraction Strips

Math Tool: Fraction Strips

1

$\frac{1}{2}$	$\frac{1}{2}$

$\frac{1}{3}$	$\frac{1}{3}$	$\frac{1}{3}$

$\frac{1}{4}$	$\frac{1}{4}$	$\frac{1}{4}$	$\frac{1}{4}$

$\frac{1}{5}$	$\frac{1}{5}$	$\frac{1}{5}$	$\frac{1}{5}$	$\frac{1}{5}$

$\frac{1}{6}$	$\frac{1}{6}$	$\frac{1}{6}$	$\frac{1}{6}$	$\frac{1}{6}$	$\frac{1}{6}$

$\frac{1}{8}$	$\frac{1}{8}$	$\frac{1}{8}$	$\frac{1}{8}$	$\frac{1}{8}$	$\frac{1}{8}$	$\frac{1}{8}$	$\frac{1}{8}$

$\frac{1}{10}$	$\frac{1}{10}$	$\frac{1}{10}$	$\frac{1}{10}$	$\frac{1}{10}$	$\frac{1}{10}$	$\frac{1}{10}$	$\frac{1}{10}$	$\frac{1}{10}$	$\frac{1}{10}$

$\frac{1}{12}$	$\frac{1}{12}$	$\frac{1}{12}$	$\frac{1}{12}$	$\frac{1}{12}$	$\frac{1}{12}$	$\frac{1}{12}$	$\frac{1}{12}$	$\frac{1}{12}$	$\frac{1}{12}$	$\frac{1}{12}$	$\frac{1}{12}$

Math Tool: Fraction Strips

1

$\frac{1}{2}$	$\frac{1}{2}$

$\frac{1}{3}$	$\frac{1}{3}$	$\frac{1}{3}$

$\frac{1}{4}$	$\frac{1}{4}$	$\frac{1}{4}$	$\frac{1}{4}$

$\frac{1}{5}$	$\frac{1}{5}$	$\frac{1}{5}$	$\frac{1}{5}$	$\frac{1}{5}$

$\frac{1}{6}$	$\frac{1}{6}$	$\frac{1}{6}$	$\frac{1}{6}$	$\frac{1}{6}$	$\frac{1}{6}$

$\frac{1}{8}$	$\frac{1}{8}$	$\frac{1}{8}$	$\frac{1}{8}$	$\frac{1}{8}$	$\frac{1}{8}$	$\frac{1}{8}$	$\frac{1}{8}$

$\frac{1}{10}$	$\frac{1}{10}$	$\frac{1}{10}$	$\frac{1}{10}$	$\frac{1}{10}$	$\frac{1}{10}$	$\frac{1}{10}$	$\frac{1}{10}$	$\frac{1}{10}$	$\frac{1}{10}$

$\frac{1}{12}$	$\frac{1}{12}$	$\frac{1}{12}$	$\frac{1}{12}$	$\frac{1}{12}$	$\frac{1}{12}$	$\frac{1}{12}$	$\frac{1}{12}$	$\frac{1}{12}$	$\frac{1}{12}$	$\frac{1}{12}$	$\frac{1}{12}$

Math Tool: Fraction Strips

1

$\frac{1}{2}$	$\frac{1}{2}$

$\frac{1}{3}$	$\frac{1}{3}$	$\frac{1}{3}$

$\frac{1}{4}$	$\frac{1}{4}$	$\frac{1}{4}$	$\frac{1}{4}$

$\frac{1}{5}$	$\frac{1}{5}$	$\frac{1}{5}$	$\frac{1}{5}$	$\frac{1}{5}$

$\frac{1}{6}$	$\frac{1}{6}$	$\frac{1}{6}$	$\frac{1}{6}$	$\frac{1}{6}$	$\frac{1}{6}$

$\frac{1}{8}$	$\frac{1}{8}$	$\frac{1}{8}$	$\frac{1}{8}$	$\frac{1}{8}$	$\frac{1}{8}$	$\frac{1}{8}$	$\frac{1}{8}$

$\frac{1}{10}$	$\frac{1}{10}$	$\frac{1}{10}$	$\frac{1}{10}$	$\frac{1}{10}$	$\frac{1}{10}$	$\frac{1}{10}$	$\frac{1}{10}$	$\frac{1}{10}$	$\frac{1}{10}$

$\frac{1}{12}$	$\frac{1}{12}$	$\frac{1}{12}$	$\frac{1}{12}$	$\frac{1}{12}$	$\frac{1}{12}$	$\frac{1}{12}$	$\frac{1}{12}$	$\frac{1}{12}$	$\frac{1}{12}$	$\frac{1}{12}$	$\frac{1}{12}$

Math Tool: Coordinate Grids

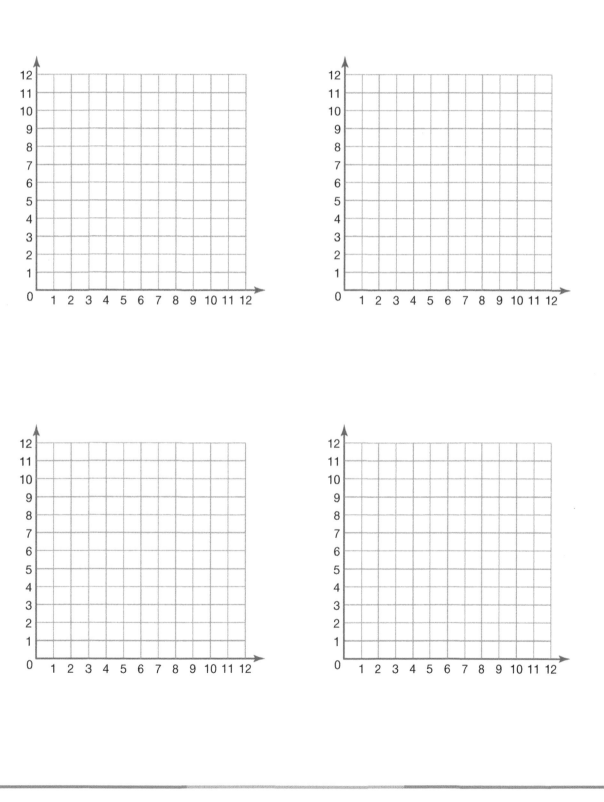

Math Tool: Decimal Place-Value Chart

Tens	Ones	Decimal Point	Tenths	Hundredths	Thousandths

Tens	Ones	Decimal Point	Tenths	Hundredths	Thousandths

Math Tool: Two-Color Counters

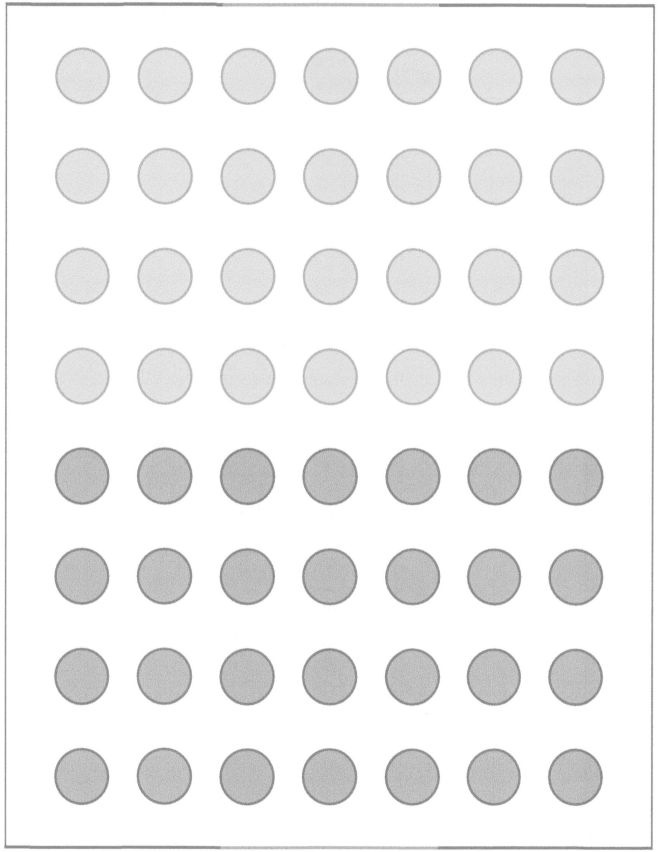

Name _____ Date _____

Math Tool: Counters

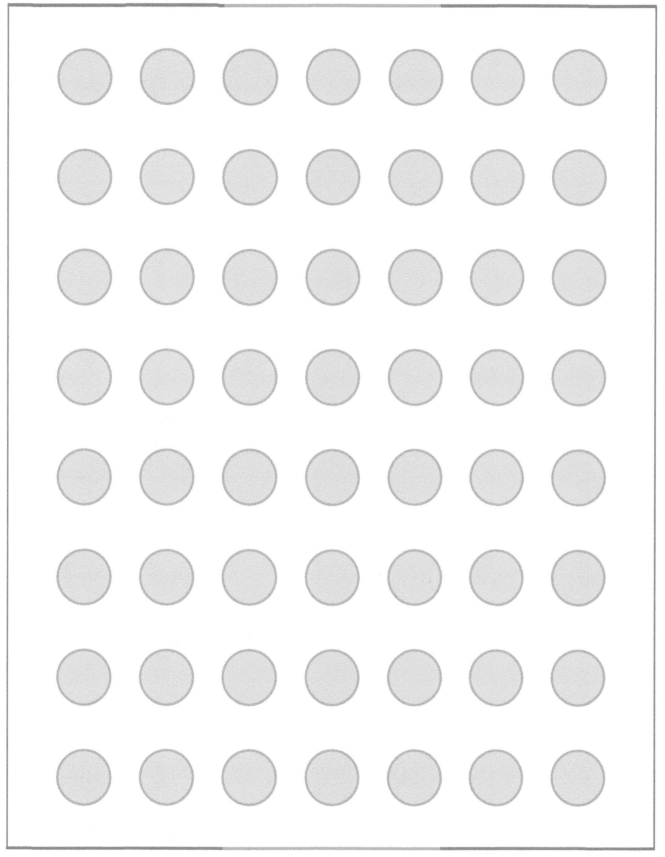

Math Tool: Number Lines

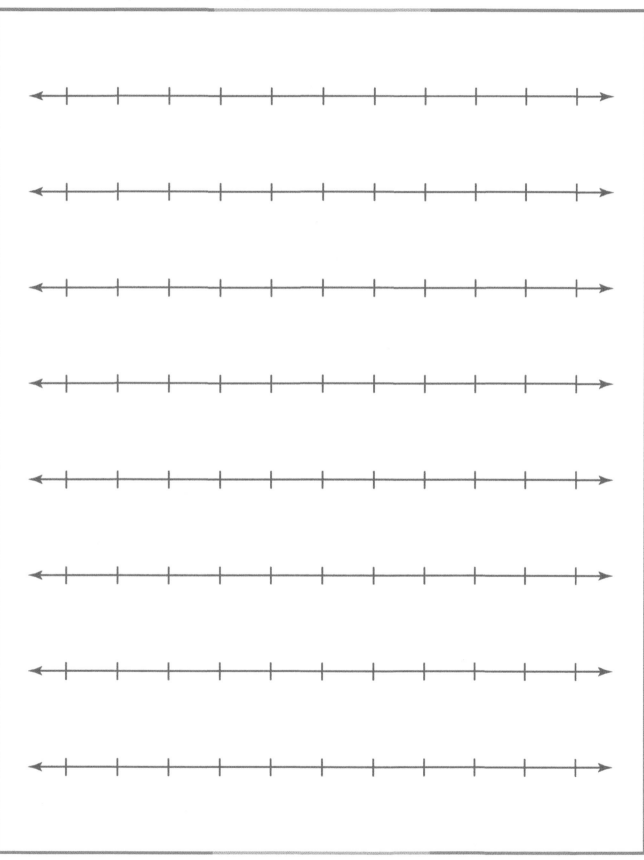

Math Tool: Number Lines

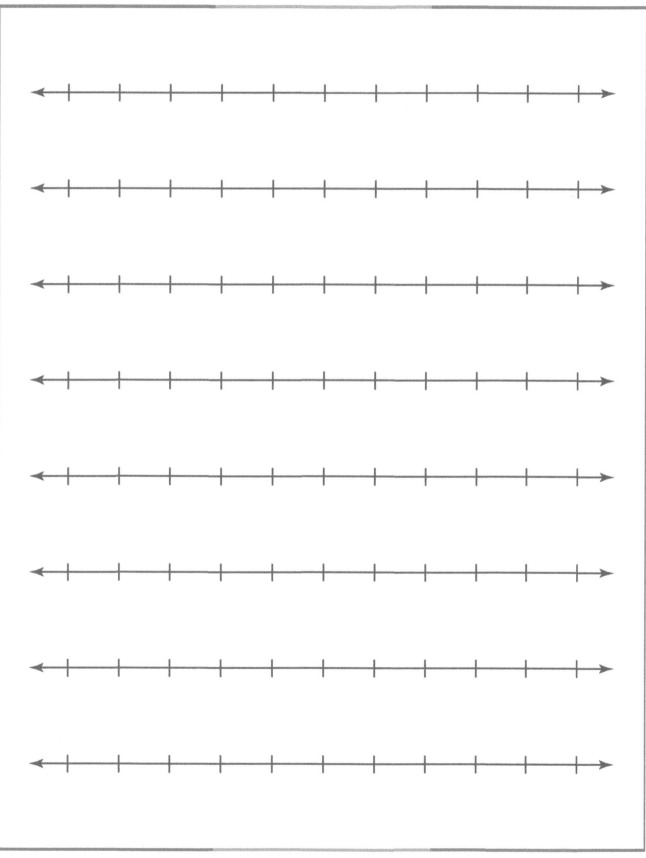

Math Tool: Number Lines

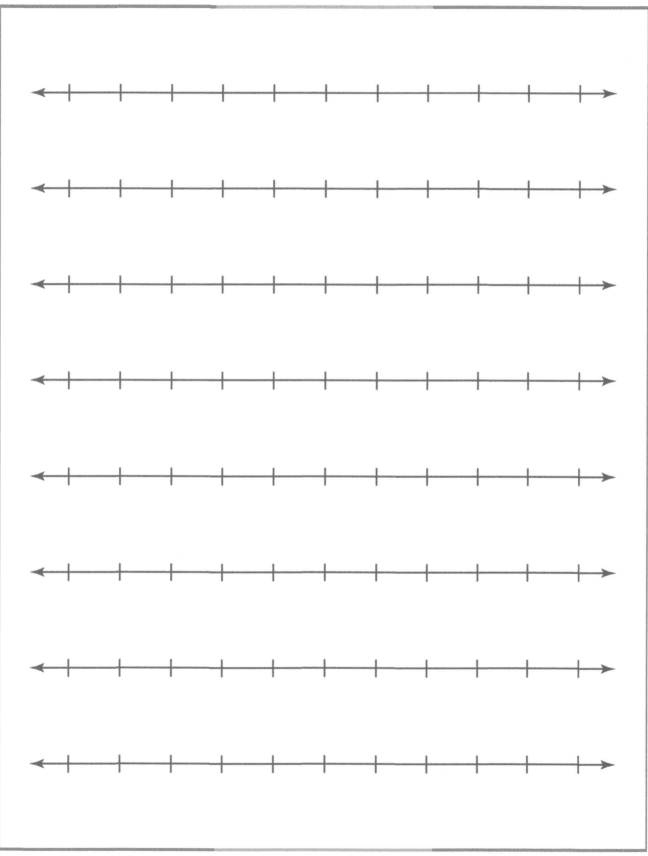

Math Tool: Number Lines

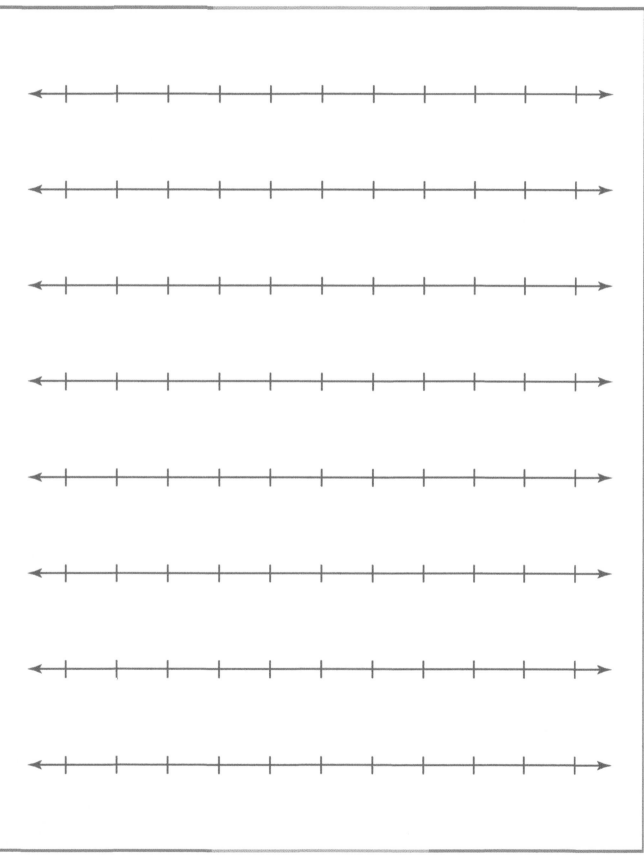

Math Tool: Number Lines

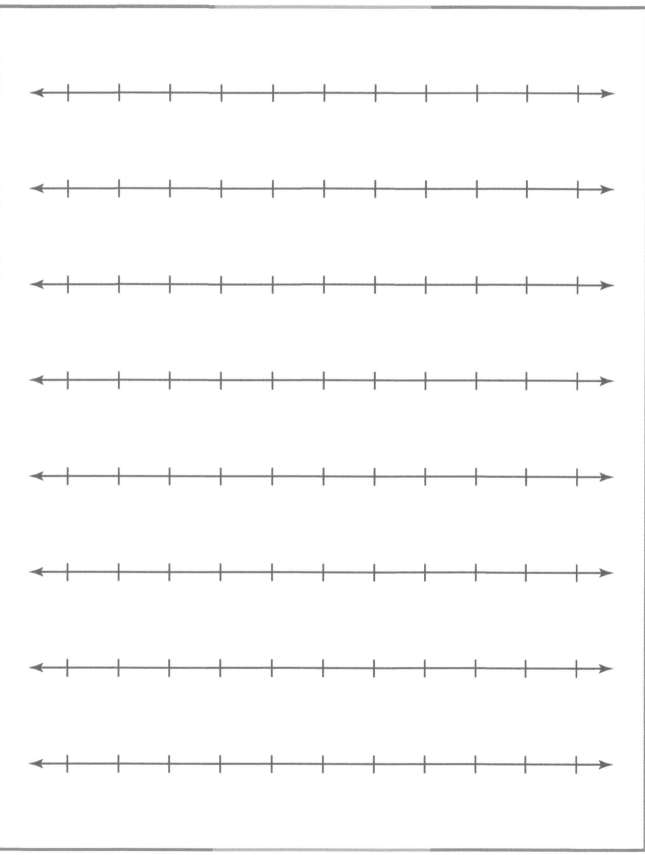

Name _____ Date _____

Math Tool: Number Lines

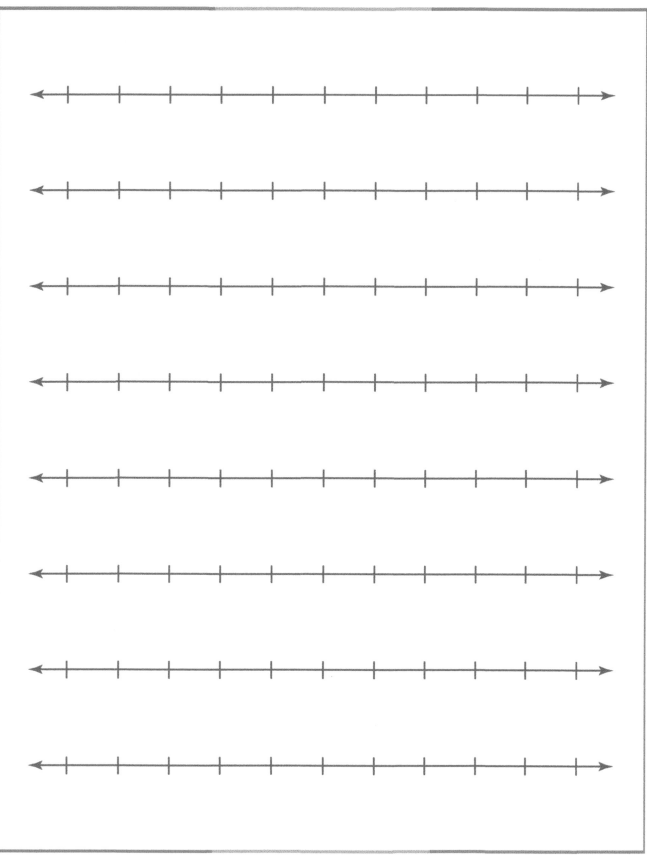

Math Tool: Number Cards

1	2
3	4
5	6
7	8
9	

Math Tool: Number Cards

1	2
3	4
5	6
7	8
9	

Math Tool: **Number Cube**

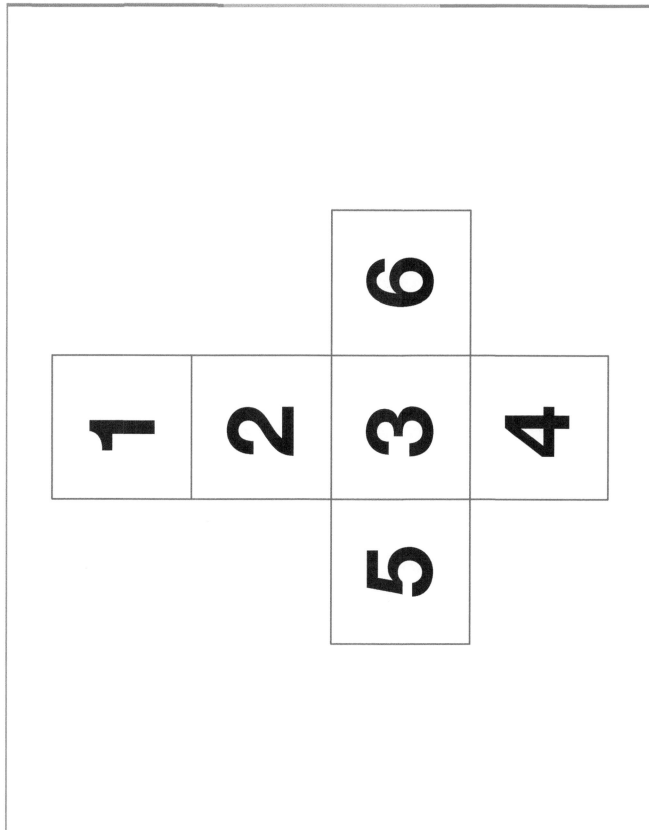

Name _____   Date _____

Math Tool: **Number Cube**

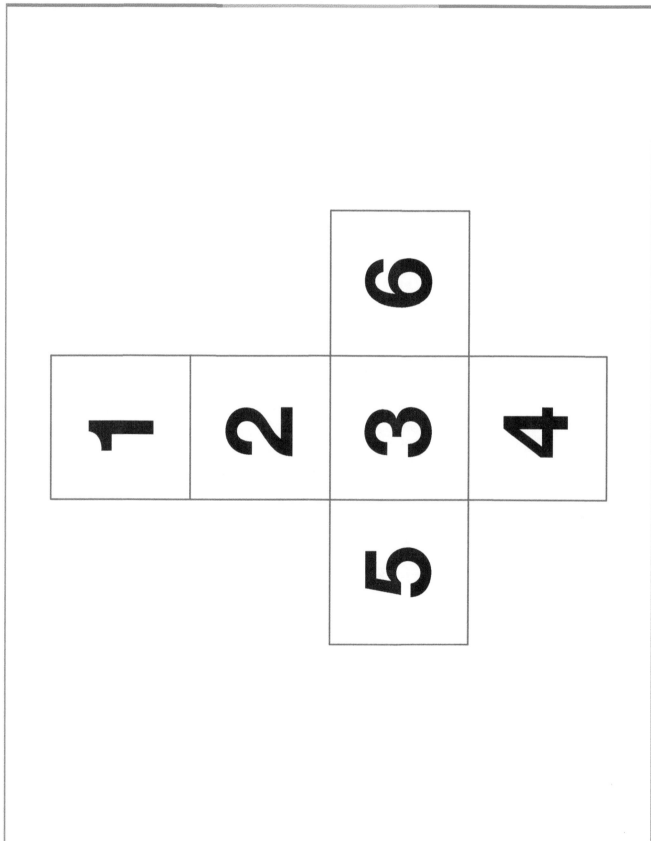

Math Tool: Number Cube

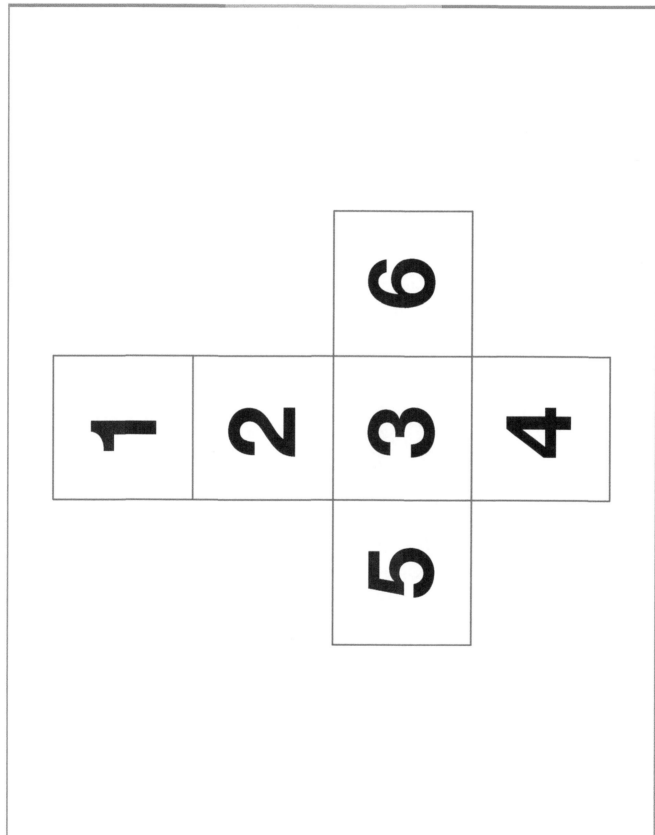

Math Tool: Circle Formulas

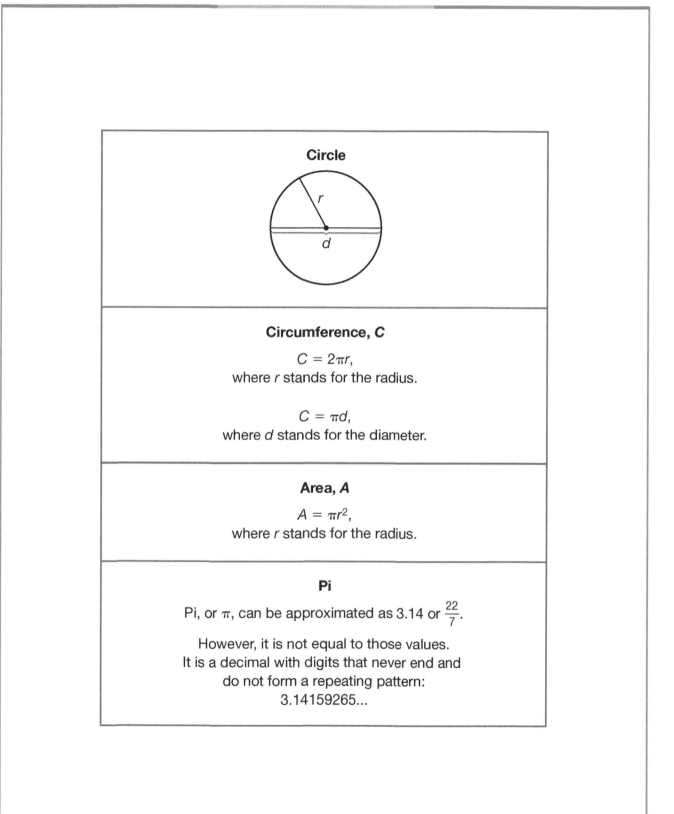

Circle

r

d

Circumference, C

$C = 2\pi r$,
where r stands for the radius.

$C = \pi d$,
where d stands for the diameter.

Area, A

$A = \pi r^2$,
where r stands for the radius.

Pi

Pi, or π, can be approximated as 3.14 or $\frac{22}{7}$.

However, it is not equal to those values.
It is a decimal with digits that never end and
do not form a repeating pattern:
3.14159265...

Math Tool: Formulas for Area, *A*

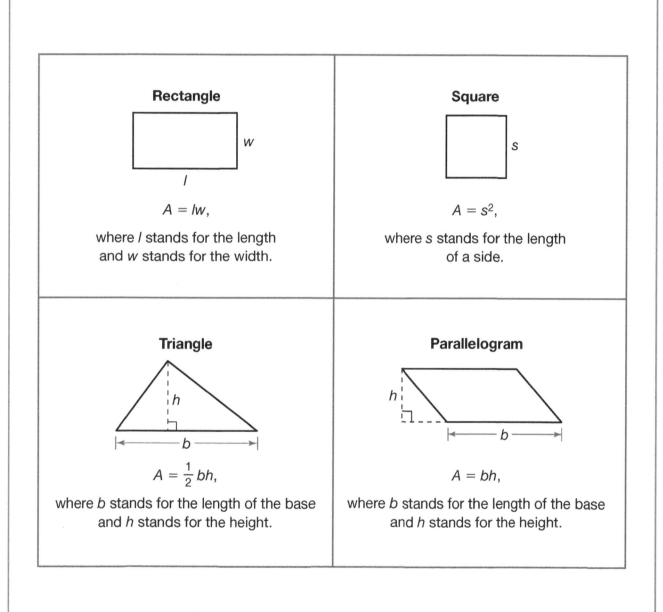

Rectangle

w

l

$A = lw,$

where *l* stands for the length
and *w* stands for the width.

Square

s

$A = s^2,$

where *s* stands for the length
of a side.

Triangle

h

b

$A = \frac{1}{2}bh,$

where *b* stands for the length of the base
and *h* stands for the height.

Parallelogram

h

b

$A = bh,$

where *b* stands for the length of the base
and *h* stands for the height.

Math Tool: Formulas for Volume, *V*

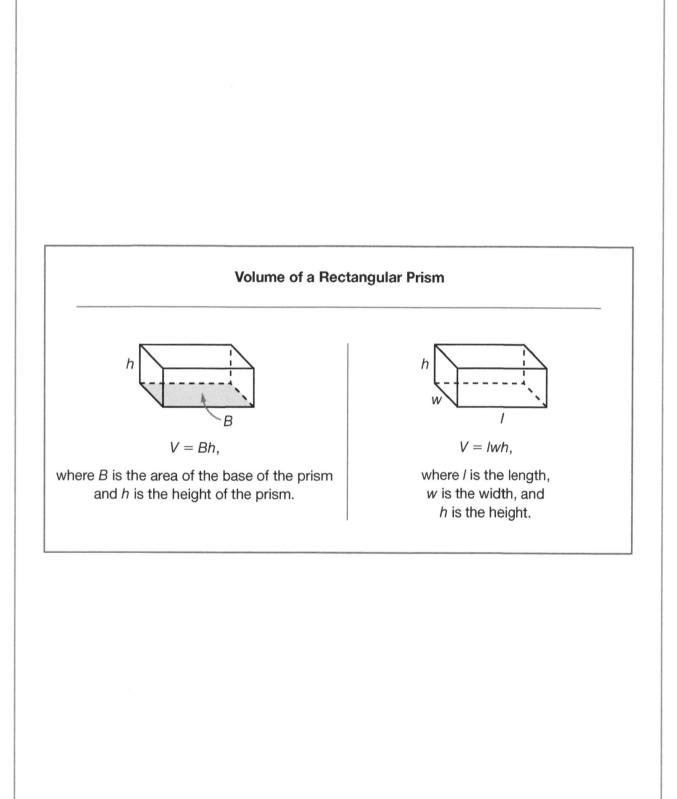

Volume of a Rectangular Prism

$V = Bh,$

where *B* is the area of the base of the prism and *h* is the height of the prism.

$V = lwh,$

where *l* is the length, *w* is the width, and *h* is the height.

Name _____ Date _____

Math Tool: Grid Paper

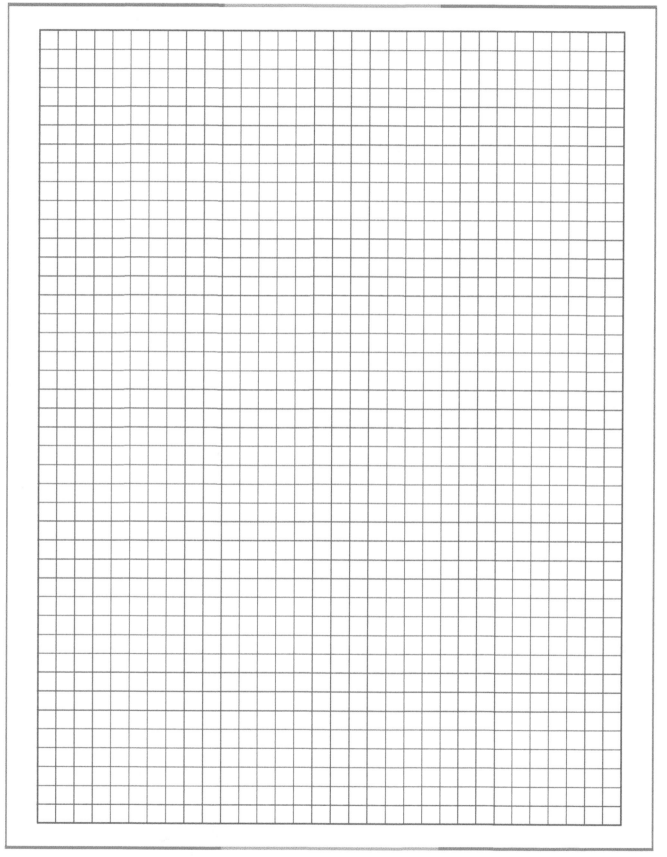

Name _____ Date _____

Math Tool: Grid Paper

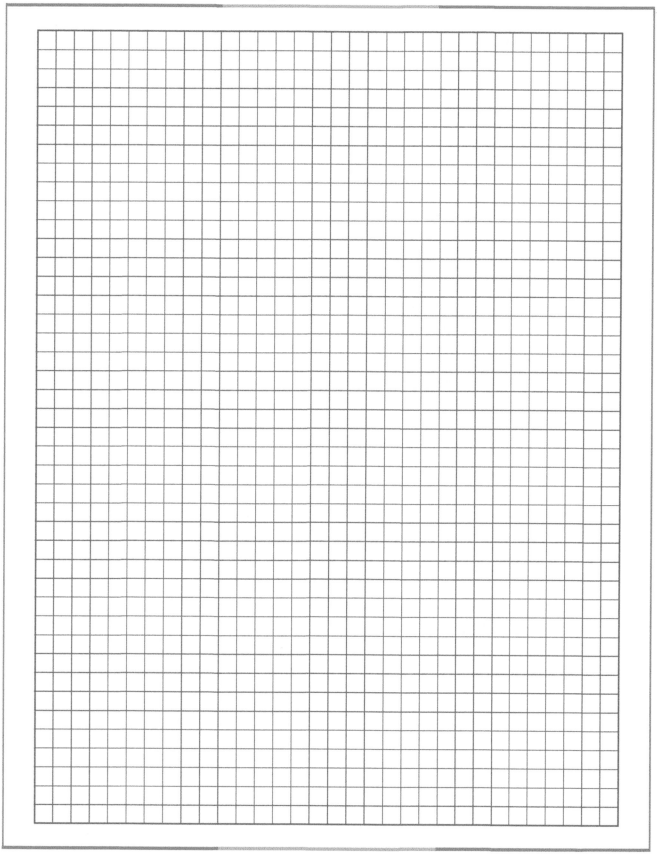

255

Math Tool: Hundred Grids

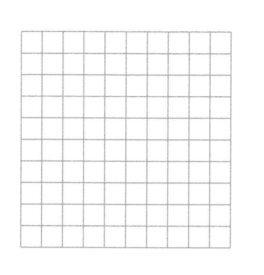

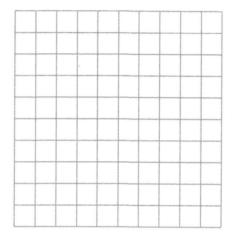

Math Tool: Spinners

Directions:
- Label the spinner.
- Place a paper clip and pencil point on the center.
- Flick paper clip with your finger to spin.

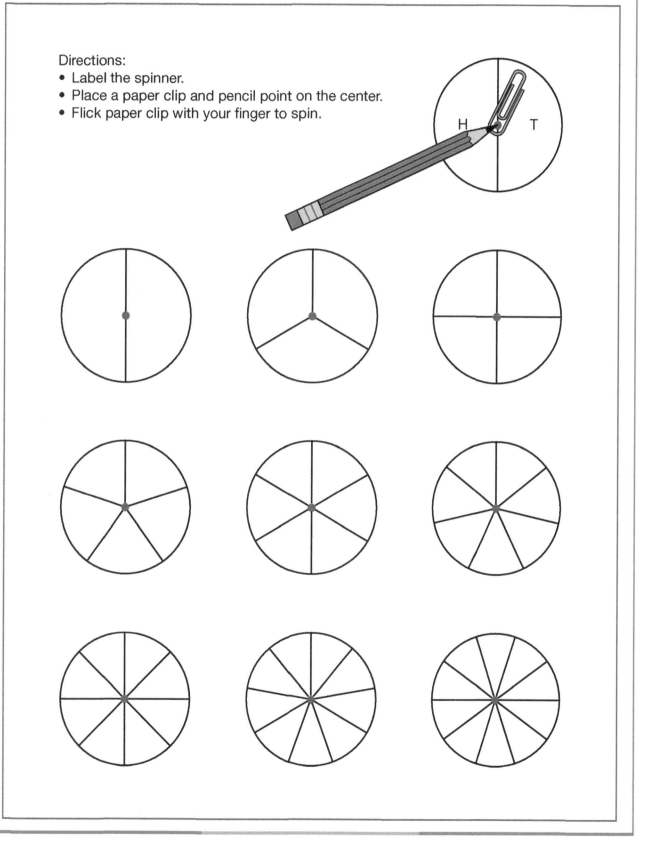

Math Tool: Spinners

Directions:
- Label the spinner.
- Place a paper clip and pencil point on the center.
- Flick paper clip with your finger to spin.

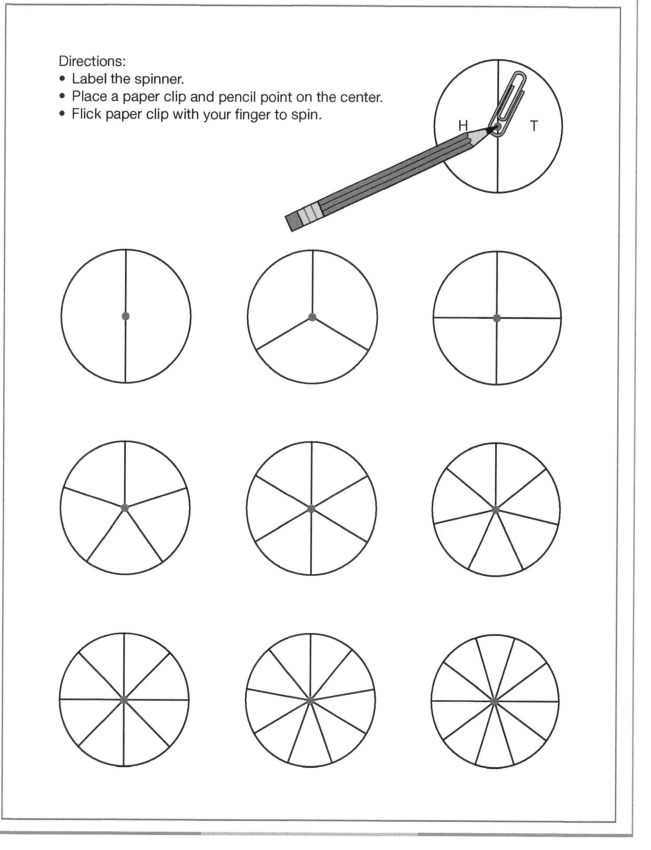

Name _____   Date _____

Math Tool: Counters

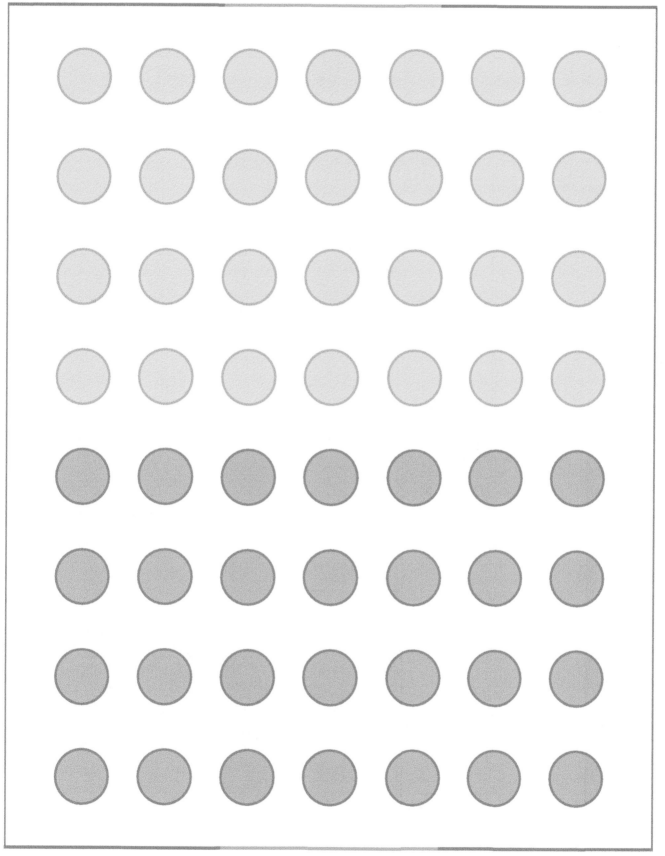

Math Tool: Grouping Mat

Name ______________________________ Date ______________

Math Tool: Centimeter Grid

Math Tool: Number Cube

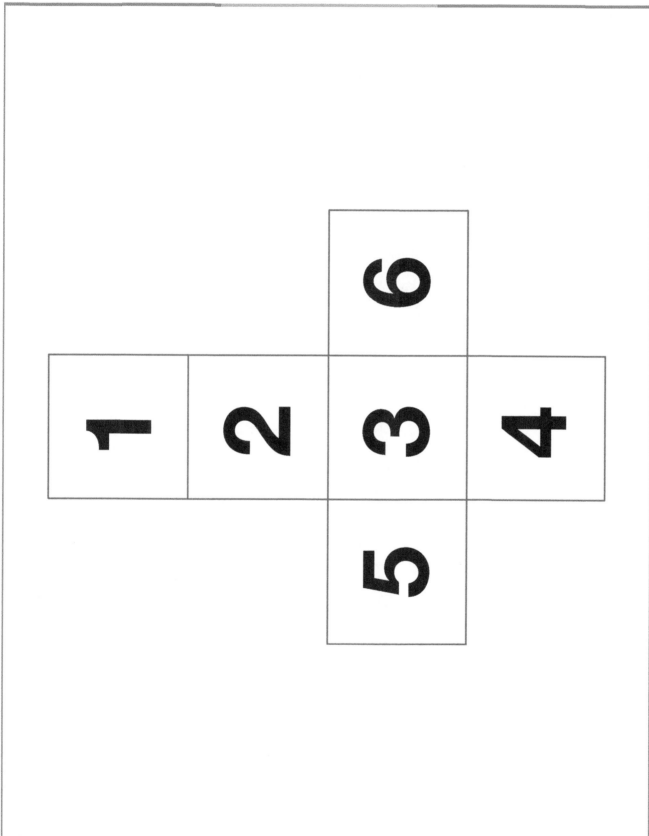

Math Tool: Net of Rectangular Prism

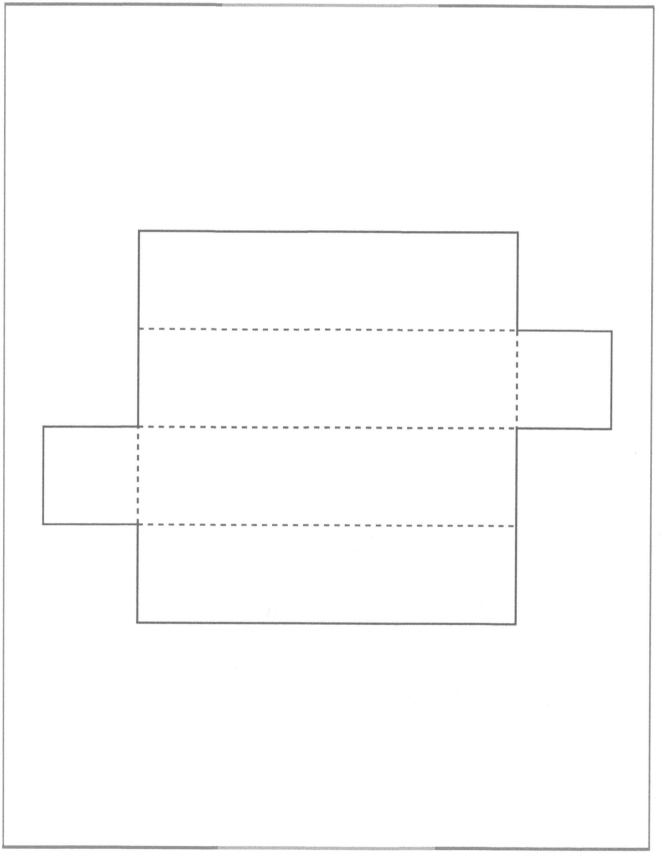